# SRA

# BUILDING
# Vocabulary
# *Skills*

## Level 4
## Student Edition

*Columbus, OH • Chicago, IL • Redmond, WA*

The **McGraw·Hill** Companies

**www.sra4kids.com**

 **SRA**

Send all inquiries to:
SRA/McGraw-Hill
4400 Easton Commons
Columbus, OH 43219

Printed in the United States of America.

ISBN 0-07-579615-5

7 8 9 QPD 09 08 07

# Table of Contents

# Unit 3

# Unit 4

1. **consequence**
(kon´ si kwens´) *n.*
result of an action

2. **scheme**
(skēm) *n.*
a secret plan

3. **venture**
(ven´ chər) *v.*
to do regardless of
the risk

4. **forbidden**
(fər bi´ dən) *adj.*
not allowed

5. **uncertain**
(un sûr´ tən) *adj.*
not sure

6. **cautious**
(ko´ shəs) *adj.*
careful

7. **unbearable**
(un bâr´ ə bəl) *adj.*
very hard to put
up with

8. **challenge**
(chal´ ənj) *n.*
a difficult situation

9. **impulse**
(im´ puls´) *n.*
a quick action
based on feeling

10. **daring**
(dâr´ ing) *adj.*
fearless

# Risks and Consequences

 **Word Meanings**

## Defining a Word

 Write the correct vocabulary word in the blank. (**Hint:** The underlined clues are related to the meaning of each word.)

1. Harriet Tubman was a _____ slave <u>who was not afraid to fight for her freedom</u>.

2. In 1849, she mapped out a _____ for escaping to Philadelphia, being careful to keep <u>her plan a secret</u>.

3. Slaves were _____ from leaving their owner's land; even the states had <u>rules against it</u>.

4. A slave who chose to _____ off the plantation was punished for <u>taking such a risk</u>.

5. Slaves wanted to escape because their lives were

    _____; they faced <u>poor living conditions and cruel treatment from slave owners</u>.

6. A slave owner might act on an _____ and hurt or insult a slave <u>in a moment of anger</u>.

7. To succeed in escaping, Harriet Tubman knew she had <u>to

    be confident in her abilities and not</u> _____ about them.

8. The _____ of being captured by slave hunters was <u>being returned to the plantation or even killed</u>!

9. Fortunately, Harriet Tubman was never captured because

    she was _____ and <u>carefully covered her tracks</u>.

10. Although, the <u>long, hard journey</u> to freedom was a

    _____, she succeeded and lived to help other slaves escape, too.

## ② Reference Skills
# Dictionary Entries

These symbols stand for parts of speech in the dictionary entry.

| | | |
|---|---|---|
| *n.* = noun | *adj.* = adjective | *v.* = verb |

 Look up each of the following vocabulary words in the dictionary. Write *n., v.,* or *adj.* in the blank. Some words have more than one part of speech.

1. challenge _____

2. scheme _____

3. cautious _____

4. venture _____

5. consequence _____

6. uncertain _____

• • • • • • • • • • • • • • • • • • • • • • • • • • • • • • • • • • • • •

 Write the vocabulary word that agrees with the part of speech and its definition.

7. *v.* _____ "to invite to participate in a contest"

8. *adj.* _____ "characterized by being careful"

9. *n.* _____ "result of an action"

10. *v.* _____ "to make a plan"

11. *n.* _____ "risky undertaking"

12. *adj.* _____ "not sure"

## Vocabulary List

1. consequence
2. scheme
3. venture
4. forbidden
5. uncertain
6. cautious
7. unbearable
8. challenge
9. impulse
10. daring

# 3 Build New Vocabulary

## Related Words

 Write the vocabulary word that is related to each word below.

| Related Word | Vocabulary Word |
| --- | --- |
| 1. impulsive | _____ |
| 2. challenger | _____ |
| 3. bear | _____ |
| 4. venturesome | _____ |
| 5. forbid | _____ |
| 6. dare | _____ |
| 7. certainly | _____ |
| 8. consequential | _____ |

 Read each sentence. Fill in the blank with a word from the **Related Word** list above that matches the underlined clues in each sentence below.

9. Pablo Picasso was a _____ artist <u>who wasn't afraid to take risks</u>.

10. His unusual work _____ changed the world of art, <u>without a doubt</u>.

11. Picasso would _____ other artists, who were <u>not as brave</u>, to paint using large shapes in place of lifelike pictures.

12. He was _____, and would <u>quickly change</u> from using all blues in his work to mostly pinks.

## Word Play

# Crossword Puzzle

 Complete the crossword puzzle below using the vocabulary words.

**DOWN**

1. follows directly from your actions
2. a plot planned over time
3. acting with care
4. full of courage
5. could go one way or the other
9. extremely difficult to withstand

**ACROSS**

6. to go boldly on a journey
7. a call to fight
8. sudden action taken without thinking
10. kept from doing something

# Vocabulary for Rules

## Vocabulary List

1. **establish**
(e stab′ lish) *v.*
to set up

2. **obedient**
(ō bē′ dē ənt) *adj.*
willing to follow
orders

3. **stubborn**
(stub′ ərn) *adj.*
not giving in

4. **privilege**
(priv′ə lij) *n.*
a special right

5. **model**
(mod′ əl) *v.*
to serve as
an example

6. **penalty**
(pen′ əl tē) *n.*
a punishment

7. **etiquette**
(et′ i kit) *n.*
rules for good
behavior

8. **relax**
(ri laks′) *v.*
to loosen

9. **exempt**
(eg zempt′) *adj.*
free from

10. **abolish**
(ə bol′ ish) *v.*
to put an end to

### 1 Word Meanings

## Example Sentences

 Read each sentence. Fill in the blanks using the vocabulary words.

1. If you make the rules more flexible to allow for

    exceptions, you _____ the rules.

2. To be _____ is to be willing to follow orders
    even when you disagree with them.

3. You can _____ good behavior by showing
    others how to act by example.

4. If we decide to _____ the rule, it will no
    longer exist.

5. It is wise to _____ a good relationship with
    your teacher at the beginning of the year.

6. A _____ is the price you pay for breaking
    the rules.

7. _____ attitudes can help you work toward
    something without giving up.

8. If you are _____ from taking the spelling
    test, you do not have to take it.

9. My _____ in our classroom this week is to
    be the line leader.

10. The teacher reviewed proper _____ with his
    students before the guest speaker arrived.

## 2 Reference Skills
# Alphabetical Order

Write the vocabulary words in alphabetical order below. Be sure to spell the words correctly.

1. _____     6. _____

2. _____     7. _____

3. _____     8. _____

4. _____     9. _____

5. _____     10. _____

• • • • • • • • • • • • • • • • • • • • • • • • • • • • • • • • • • •

Look at each vocabulary word and its synonym below. Write the word that comes first alphabetically in the blank. Put a check mark in the box to show how many letters you had to look at in each word in order to put them in alphabetical order.

**11.** manners, etiquette

_____  ☐1 ☐2 ☐3

**12.** penalty, punishment

_____  ☐1 ☐2 ☐3

**13.** excused, exempt

_____  ☐1 ☐2 ☐3

**14.** relax, loosen

_____  ☐1 ☐2 ☐3

## Vocabulary List

1. *establish*
2. *obedient*
3. *stubborn*
4. *privilege*
5. *model*
6. *penalty*
7. *etiquette*
8. *relax*
9. *exempt*
10. *abolish*

# 3 Build New Vocabulary

## Analogies

Read the pairs of words below and determine the relationship between them. Fill in the blank with the appropriate vocabulary word that agrees with the relationship and completes the analogy.

1. *lose* is to *find* as *end* is to _____

2. *automobile* is to *vehicle* as *punishment* is to

   _____

3. *erase* is to *delete* as *excused* is to _____

4. *cooperate* is to *rebel* as *tighten* is to _____

5. *find* is to *locate* as *represent* is to _____

6. *worried* is to *carefree* as *disobedient* is to

   _____

7. *lead* is to *follow* as *establish* is to _____

8. *villain* is to *hero* as *rudeness* is to _____

9. *event* is to *occasion* as *right* is to _____

10. *unusual* is to *unique* as *willful* is to _____

• • • • • • • • • • • • • • • • • • • • • • • • • • • • • • • • • • • • • •

## Think About It

The first step in solving analogies is to uncover the relationship between the words in the first set. If they are antonyms, the words in the second set will be antonyms, also. If the words in the first set are synonyms, the words in the second set will also be synonyms.

 ## Word Play

# Tongue Twisters

 Use the vocabulary words to complete each of these tongue twisters.

1. Abraham Lincoln advocated that America

   _____ the act of slavery for all time.

2. Paul's posted _____ is to pass out papers to his peers.

3. Reggie's request was to _____ the rule regarding running at recess.

4. The energetic attorney will _____ existing evidence every evening.

5. My older sister Olivia is _____ on every occasion.

6. The endangered African elephant is _____ from legal execution.

7. Princess Emily's education was made evident by her eating

   _____ at the royal event.

8. The _____ for poaching in the Newfoundland province is payment or prison.

9. Sylvia said she is sorry, but she is not sharing her strawberries with Saul. Sometimes she is so

   _____ .

10. Manny's mother will _____ her mastery of the mandolin on Monday.

## Vocabulary for Growing Up

### ① Word Meanings

## Synonyms and Antonyms

 Read each word or phrase below. Write the appropriate vocabulary word that is either the synonym or antonym of each word or phrase in the blank.

1. to know what is right (synonym) _____

2. goal (synonym) _____

3. hopelessness (antonym) _____

4. grow (synonym) _____

5. irresponsible (antonym) _____

6. mingle (synonym) _____

7. something passed on (synonym) _____

8. immaturity (antonym) _____

9. persuade (synonym) _____

10. respect (synonym) _____

### Think About It

Using a thesaurus to find synonyms and antonyms can make your vocabulary more exciting. When you are writing a story, look up repeated words in your thesaurus to keep your reader interested.

**Vocabulary List**

1. **expectations**
(ek´ spek tā´ shənz) n.
reasons for hoping

2. **influence**
(in´ floo əns) n.
power to affect other

3. **socialize**
(so´ shə līz) v.
to act friendly with others

4. **develop**
(di vel´ əp) v.
to grow

5. **conscience**
(kon´ shəns) n.
ability to understand right from wrong

6. **maturity**
(mə choor´ i tē) n.
reaching full growth

7. **esteem**
(e stēm´) v.
to consider good

8. **trustworthy**
(trust´ wûr´ thē) adj.
can be depended upon

9. **heredity**
(hə red´ i tē) n.
family likeness

10. **aspiration**
(as´ pə rā shən) n.
a high goal

# ② Reference Skills
## Guide Words

 Look at each set of guide words. Write the vocabulary word that would be found on that page.

1. hamburger – history

   _____

2. trumpet – umbrella

   _____

3. lunch – motorcycle

   _____

4. cupcake – dolphin

   _____

5. skeleton – squid

   _____

6. alphabet – baboon

   _____

7. energy – exercise

   _____

8. hour – jazz

   _____

9. cartoon – crocodile

   _____

10. exit – fraction

   _____

## Vocabulary List

1. expectations
2. influence
3. socialize
4. develop
5. conscience
6. maturity
7. esteem
8. trustworthy
9. heredity
10. aspiration

# 3 Build New Vocabulary

## Nouns and Verbs

 Using the vocabulary words, write the noun forms of the following verbs.

1. aspire _____

2. expect _____

3. mature _____

4. influence _____

· · · · · · · · · · · · · · · · · · · · · · · · · · · · · · · · · · · · ·

Complete the following sentences using the verb and noun forms of the vocabulary words from above.

5. A student who is _____ shows her

   _____ through self-discipline.

6. I _____ to break Tony Hawk's world record of completing the most midair skateboard rotations. My

   _____ is to successfully land three full rotations.

7. He will _____ her to volunteer, and

   she probably will have the same _____ on someone else.

8. My grandfather will _____ that we have already cleaned the garage; that is just one of his

   _____ of my sister and me.

Score _____ (Top Score 12)   Vocabulary for Growing Up • Build New Vocabulary

# 4 Word Play

## Riddles

 Read the riddles below. Write the vocabulary word in the blank that best solves each riddle.

**1.** I am what humans will do all their lives. They can do it physically, mentally, and emotionally. What am I?

_____

**2.** I am a little voice that tries to tell you to stop when you are doing something wrong. What am I? _____

**3.** I am what makes a baby look like its mother and father. What am I? _____

**4.** I am what you have for yourself that gives you hope for something in the future. What am I? _____

**5.** I am the power to cause others to think, feel, or act a certain way. What am I? _____

**6.** I am what you feel toward a person or thing that you respect and consider good. What am I?

_____

**7.** I am what people call you because they can depend on you. What am I? _____

**8.** I am what you would do if you wanted to get to know a group of people better. What am I?

_____

**9.** I am what you can set for yourself before you begin to work toward something. What am I?

_____

**10.** I am the full growth of something. What am I?

_____

## Vocabulary List

1. **giddy**
(gid´ ē) *adj.*
silly

2. **mellow**
(mel´ ō) *adj.*
calm

3. **irritable**
(ir´ i tə bəl) *adj.*
close to getting angry

4. **humiliated**
(hū mil´ ē āt əd) *adj.*
feeling foolish

5. **anxious**
(angk´ shəs) *adj.*
worried

6. **enraged**
(en rājd´) *adj.*
made angry

7. **delighted**
(di lī´ tid) *adj.*
pleased

8. **gloomy**
(gloo͞´ mē) *adj.*
sad

9. **affectionate**
(ə fek´ shə nit) *adj.*
loving

10. **content**
(kən tent´) *adj.*
wanting nothing else

# Moods and Feelings

**1**  **Word Meanings**

## Categorizing

  Write the vocabulary word that describes the mood of each person in the sentences below.

1. Tanisha has been studying for her test, but she is still nervous about taking it. Tanisha is _____.

2. Charity decided that she did not want dessert after eating the five-course meal. Charity was _____.

3. Ryan is very happy because he just won the blue ribbon for his incredible dancing pig. Ryan is _____.

4. Maria is feeling sad about her older brother leaving for college next week. Maria is _____.

5. Theo was very angry when he discovered his project was not saved on the computer. Theo was _____.

6. Eric was laughing and acting silly after watching his favorite cartoon. Eric was _____.

7. Julie asked us not to bother her this morning because she is feeling grumpy. Julie is _____.

8. After taking a nap on the beach, Sara was calm and relaxed. Sara was _____.

9. Brandon was embarrassed when he forgot his song at the piano recital. Brandon was _____.

10. Lauren cuddled and played with her new puppy lovingly. Lauren was _____.

## ② Reference Skills

# Using a Thesaurus

Using a thesaurus, place a check mark next to the synonym that agrees with the vocabulary word given.

1. humiliated ☐ embarrassed ☐ frozen
2. delighted ☐ little ☐ pleased
3. enraged ☐ angered ☐ released
4. mellow ☐ yellow ☐ relaxed
5. gloomy ☐ unhappy ☐ sticky
6. anxious ☐ upset ☐ playful
7. giddy ☐ ill ☐ silly
8. irritable ☐ cranky ☐ huge
9. affectionate ☐ caring ☐ boring
10. content ☐ friendly ☐ satisfied

• • • • • • • • • • • • • • • • • • • • • • • • • • • • • • • • • • • •

Match the vocabulary words with their definitions.

11. _____ irritable        A. wanting nothing else

12. _____ enraged          B. worried

13. _____ affectionate     C. calm

14. _____ giddy            D. sad

15. _____ anxious          E. feeling foolish

16. _____ gloomy           F. silly

17. _____ content          G. pleased

18. _____ mellow           H. loving

19. _____ delighted        I. close to getting angry

20. _____ humiliated       J. made angry

## Vocabulary List

1. *giddy*
2. *mellow*
3. *irritable*
4. *humiliated*
5. *anxious*
6. *enraged*
7. *delighted*
8. *gloomy*
9. *affectionate*
10. *content*

# 3 Build New Vocabulary

## Adverb Forms

Add the suffix *-ly* to the vocabulary words below to form adverbs. Write each adverb in the blank and draw a line to its matching definition. Use a dictionary to check your spelling.

1. affectionate _____        **A.** sadly or depressingly

2. anxious _____            **B.** with love and tenderness

3. irritable _____           **C.** done in a calm manner

4. gloomy _____             **D.** done with an angry manner

5. mellow _____            **E.** with impatience

Use the adverbs you formed above to complete the following sentences.

6. Carmen _____ grumbled all the way back to bed after getting up to answer the phone late last night.

7. The guests hid in the dark, _____ waiting for the surprise party to begin.

8. Hong stared _____ out the window after hearing that recess would be indoors today.

9. Vanessa held her baby sister _____ while she fed her a bottle.

10. The tired, old dog lay _____ on the front porch.

**4** Word Play

# Similes

 Complete each simile by underlining the appropriate vocabulary word in parentheses.

1. as (enraged, mellow) as an angry bee

2. as (irritable, content) as a baby with a full belly and a

   warm blanket

3. as (delighted, enraged) as a bear with a pot of honey

4. as (giddy, gloomy) as a clown at the circus

5. as (anxious, mellow) as a cat taking a nap in the sun

• • • • • • • • • • • • • • • • • • • • • • • • • • • • • • • • • • • • • •

Find the simile that relates to the meaning of each underlined vocabulary word. Fill in the blank with the letter of the correct simile.

6. The child was as <u>affectionate</u> as _____.
   **A.** an apple falling off a tree
   **B.** a doe with her fawn
   **C.** the boat on the water

7. My brother was as <u>irritable</u> as _____.
   **A.** a hungry bear
   **B.** a shiny red bike
   **C.** a flower in spring

8. My uncle was as <u>mellow</u> as _____.
   **A.** a hummingbird
   **B.** a chainsaw
   **C.** a lazy river

9. Her face looked as <u>gloomy</u> as _____.
   **A.** a ray of sunshine
   **B.** a rainy day at the beach
   **C.** a wrinkled raisin

10. I felt as <u>humiliated</u> as _____.
    **A.** an actor who has forgotten her lines
    **B.** a sandwich with no pickle
    **C.** a warm fire at a campsite

1. **abundance**
(ə bun′ dəns) *n.*
a large amount

2. **incredible**
(in kred′ ə bəl) *adj.*
hard to believe

3. **dreadful**
(dred′ fəl) *adj.*
awful

4. **exaggeration**
(eg zaj′ ə rā′ shən) *n.*
quality appearing greater than what is actual

5. **paramount**
(par′ ə mount′) *adj.*
above all others

6. **fantastic**
(fan tas′ tik) *adj.*
strange or unusual

7. **unspeakable**
(un spē′ kə bəl) *adj.*
too bad to talk about

8. **gigantic**
(jī gan′ tik) *adj.*
huge

9. **outermost**
(ou′ tər mōst′) *adj.*
farthest out

10. **radical**
(rad′ i kəl) *n.*
a person fighting for change

# Vocabulary for Extremes
## 1 Word Meanings
### Degrees in Definition

Write the vocabulary word that best fits in the order of degree of the words or phrases below.

1. someone who keeps things the same, someone who can be influenced, a _ _ _ _ _□_

2. tiny, medium, _ _ _ _ _□_

3. shortage, exact amount, _ _ _ _ _ _ _ _□

4. minimize, actual size, _□_ _ _ _ _ _ _ _ _

5. ordinary, odd, _ _ _□_ _ _ _ _

6. closest, nearby, _ _ _ _□_ _ _ _

7. wonderful, average, _ _ □_ _ _ _ _

8. least, normal, _ _ _ _□_ _ _ _

9. believable, interesting, _ _ _ _□_ _ _ _

10. sensational, boring, _ _□_ _ _ _ _ _

• • • • • • • • • • • • • • • • • • • • • • • • • • • • • • • • •

Write the letters in the boxes in the order they appear above to complete the following sentence.

The north pole and the south pole are magnetic because they are □ □ opposite □ □ □ □ □ □ □ □

from each other.

## ② Reference Skills

# Dictionary Entry

Look at the dictionary entry below and answer the questions that follow.

> **fan·tas·tic** (fan tas′ tik) *adj.* **1.** very strange or unusual; odd: *There are many fantastic creatures in the rain forest.* **2.** existing only in the mind; imaginary: *Lulu tells fantastic stories.* **3.** Informal. very good; splendid: *That sunset looks fantastic.* **4.** extraordinary; remarkable: *One million dollars is a fantastic amount of money.* –**fan·tas·ti·cal** (fan tas′ ti kəl). –**fan·tas·ti·cal·ly,** *adv.*

1. Entry words are given in bold type at the beginning of the entry. What is the entry word? _____

2. What part of speech is *fantastic?* _____

3. How many syllables are there in *fantastic?*

   _____

4. If you had to split the word *fantastic* at the end of a line, where could you split it?

   _____

5. Different definitions are numbered. How many definitions are given for *fantastic?* _____

6. Example sentences are often given to clarify how a word should be used. They are usually in italic type. What is the example sentence for the second definition?

   _____

7. Other word forms and their parts of speech may be given at the end of an entry. What other word forms are given for *fantastic?*

   _____

8. What part of speech is *fantastically?* _____

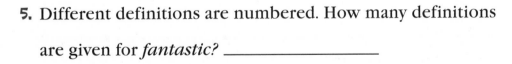

## Vocabulary List

1. *abundance*
2. *incredible*
3. *dreadful*
4. *exaggeration*
5. *paramount*
6. *fantastic*
7. *unspeakable*
8. *gigantic*
9. *outermost*
10. *radical*

# 3 Build New Vocabulary

## Context Clues

 Using context clues, replace the underlined word with one of the vocabulary words in parentheses. Write the vocabulary word in the blank.

1. A rain forest is a place of <u>preeminent</u> importance for several reasons, including its part in fighting pollution, its animals and plants that provide food, shelter, jobs, and medicines, and its beauty that is like no other place on Earth. (**dreadful, paramount, gigantic**) _____

2. When you travel through a rain forest, the <u>inconceivable</u> sounds, sights, and smells are very different and hard to believe. (**unspeakable, abundance, incredible**)

   _____

3. A <u>plethora</u> of creatures lives in the rain forest. It is home to many insects, mammals, amphibians, reptiles, and birds.

   (**abundance, fantastic, outermost**) _____

4. From the giant otter to the goliath beetle, there are <u>massive</u> creatures living in the rain forest. (**exaggeration, gigantic, paramount**) _____

5. The endangerment of the animals of the rain forest is a <u>tragic</u> result of environmental pollutants and increasing loss of habitat. (**dreadful, gigantic, abundance**)

   _____

6. It is an <u>abhorrent</u> truth that we are destroying the rain forest so quickly that if things do not change, all will be gone soon. (**gigantic, outermost, unspeakable**)

   _____

 **Word Play**

# Idioms

 Write the vocabulary word that the underlined idiom in each sentence describes.

1. The story of a 450-pound catfish is <u>beyond belief</u>.

   _____

2. There is rain <u>enough and to spare</u> in the jungle.

   _____

3. Some people think environmentalists are <u>making mountains out of molehills</u>. _____

• • • • • • • • • • • • • • • • • • • • • • • • • • • • • • • • • •

 Read each sentence below carefully. Decide what the underlined idiom means and circle the best answer.

4. When I told my best friend that I just won the grand prize for the fundraiser, he said, "Dillian, <u>stop pulling my leg</u>!"
   **A.** I was pulling my friend's right leg until he said he believed me.
   **B.** My best friend thought I was joking about winning the grand prize.
   **C.** My best friend did not want to hear me talking about winning the grand prize.

5. My neighbor is outside every afternoon. He <u>has a green thumb</u>.
   **A.** My neighbor is not embarrassed about his strange thumb.
   **B.** My neighbor is an alien.
   **C.** My neighbor enjoys gardening and working on his lawn.

6. When I called my cousins to see whether they wanted to spend the night at our house, my aunt said, "Please, get these kids <u>out of my hair</u>!"
   **A.** My cousins are really, really tiny.
   **B.** My aunt was excited about her children leaving her alone for a while.
   **C.** My aunt needed to schedule an appointment with her hairdresser.

# Vocabulary Review

## 1 Review Word Meanings

Read the passage below. Then answer the questions about the boldfaced vocabulary words.

## A Peasant's Life in the Middle Ages

Misery and hardship are two words that one can use to describe the lives of peasants in Europe during the Middle Ages. For one thing, these struggling, lower-class workers lived on what were called *manors,* which provided only some protection from outside threats. Their homes were not **gigantic** by any means (two rooms at the most), and the thatched roofs made them easy to destroy.

Secondly, peasants had few **privileges.** They were expected to give up their hard-earned money to the lord of the manor in exchange for protection. A third fact that made life at times **unbearable** for peasants was the **abundance** of health problems. Doctors were unsure about how to cure most diseases. It was a **gloomy** outlook on life for many of the peasants living during this difficult time.

Now read the following questions. Then completely fill in the bubble of the correct answer.

1. Which word is an antonym for *gigantic?*
   - Ⓐ vast
   - Ⓑ huge
   - Ⓒ tiny

2. In which sentence below is the word *privileges* correctly defined?
   - Ⓐ Peasants had few privileges, or rules.
   - Ⓑ Peasants had few privileges, or special rights.
   - Ⓒ Peasants had few privileges, or appeals.

3. If something is *unbearable*, it is
   _____.
   - Ⓐ forbidden
   - Ⓑ savage
   - Ⓒ impossible to tolerate

4. Which word is a synonym for *abundance?*
   - Ⓐ wealth
   - Ⓑ amount
   - Ⓒ incredible

5. Which sentence below does NOT support the idea that peasants during the Middle Ages had a *gloomy* outlook on life?
   - Ⓐ The struggling lower-class workers lived in isolation.
   - Ⓑ They were expected to give up their hard-earned money to the lord of the manor.
   - Ⓒ Many recipes for lovely pies and breads were created during the Middle Ages.

## ② Review Word Meanings

Read the passage below. Then answer the questions about the boldfaced vocabulary words.

# The War That Lasted One Hundred Years (or More)

Although it had been **developing** since the 1200s, what is known today as The Hundred Years' War began around 1340. Trouble started when France **challenged,** or questioned, the trade agreement between England and Flanders that allowed England to receive wine in exchange for fine cloth. France's **scheme** was to win back control of Flanders and put in place new trade requirements that would give the French people more money.

As a **consequence** of this plan, England was furious and tempted the middle-class people in Flanders into fighting the upper class, who sided with the French. The growing anger between the English and the French gradually led to the first battle in 1340. **Daring** English soldiers attacked French ships in the Netherlands. In the end, England was forced out of France almost *two hundred* years later, in 1565.

Now read the following questions. Then completely fill in the bubble of the correct answer.

1. Which answer is listed in alphabetical order?
   Ⓐ challenged, daring, developing
   Ⓑ consequenced, challenged, daring
   Ⓒ daring, challenged, consequence

2. Which example sentence would be correct in a dictionary entry for *scheme?*
   Ⓐ The scheme of her dress was made of lace.
   Ⓑ What's your scheme for winning back the money you lost?
   Ⓒ There was a scheme of students waiting to board the bus.

3. In which sentence is *daring* used the same way it is used in the passage?
   Ⓐ The daring knight defended the helpless peasant.
   Ⓑ Are you daring me to a duel?
   Ⓒ Daring someone to do something dangerous is not a good idea.

4. Which dictionary definition matches how *challenged* is used in the passage?
   Ⓐ fought with weapons
   Ⓑ doubted or called into question
   Ⓒ denied

5. Which words would be labeled *syn* in thesaurus entries for *develop, consequence,* and *scheme,* in order?
   Ⓐ grow, result, fantastic
   Ⓑ struggle, outcome, plan
   Ⓒ grow, result, plan

## Review Word Meanings

Read the passage below. Then answer the questions about the boldfaced vocabulary words.

# On Being a Knight

Stories about the Middle Ages often star brave knights and their **incredible** adventures. Knights are known for slaying dragons, but many people believe that these tales are simply **fantastic** and not based on fact. Fortunately, there is a lot more to learn about knights than just **exaggerated** reports of dragon slaying.

There were many requirements for becoming a knight—acting on good **conscience** at all times was perhaps the most important trait. Knights usually took a sacred oath to help others and rid the world of evil. A true knight felt that it was necessary to keep his word and to be kind to his fellow man. Overall, being a knight was more about being a good person than about fighting dragons and rescuing **anxious** damsels in distress.

Now read the following questions. Then completely fill in the bubble of the correct answer.

1. What is the definition of *incredible?*
   Ⓐ beautiful
   Ⓑ hard to believe
   Ⓒ having to do with credit

2. Which statement is NOT true according to the passage above?
   Ⓐ Knights are known for slaying dragons.
   Ⓑ There were many requirements for becoming a knight.
   Ⓒ Being a knight was more about fighting dragons than being a good person.

3. In which sentence is the form of *exaggerated* used correctly?
   Ⓐ Mark Twain once said, "The report of my death was an exaggeration."
   Ⓑ Mark Twain exaggerated a book called *A Connecticut Yankee in King Arthur's Court.*
   Ⓒ The exaggeration story was about the Knights of the Round Table.

4. In the passage, what does *fantastic* mean?
   Ⓐ good
   Ⓑ existing only in the imagination
   Ⓒ very large

5. In which sentence is the form of *anxious* used as a noun?
   Ⓐ I anxiously waited for my cousin to arrive.
   Ⓑ Anxiety can actually make you sick.
   Ⓒ The anxious puppy nibbled on my fingers.

## 4 Review Word Meanings

Read the passage below. Then answer the questions about the boldfaced vocabulary words.

# The Story of Saint George and the Dragon

The story begins as Una, a princess, and the Red Cross Knight **cautiously venture** out to face the dreadful dragon that has been tormenting Una's kingdom. After many days of traveling, the knight sees a glorious palace on top of a mountain. The **delighted** knight announces, "Una and I should go there at once." However, an old hermit reminds him that he must ignore his own desires and face the dragon in the valley below.

The knight and Una accept the **uncertainty** of their futures and ride into the valley to find the **dreadful** beast. After a lengthy, fierce battle, the knight overcomes all limitations and slays the dragon. The king is so pleased that he changes the knight's name to Saint George of Merry England. The knight and Una are married, and they live **contentedly** for the rest of their lives.

Now read the following questions. Then completely fill in the bubble of the correct answer.

1. Which example sentence would be correct in a dictionary entry for *venture?*
   Ⓐ The knight and the lady were ventured for life.
   Ⓑ Open the venture to let in some fresh air.
   Ⓒ May I venture a guess at the answer?

2. In which sentence is *cautiously* contrasted with its opposite meaning?
   Ⓐ Although he began his journey cautiously, the knight soon lost his fear and boldly marched forward to fight the dragon.
   Ⓑ Although he began his journey cautiously, the knight soon grew tired and stopped to rest for the evening.
   Ⓒ Although he began his journey cautiously, the knight carefully prepared to fight the dragon.

3. Which word is a synonym for *uncertainty?*
   Ⓐ unbearable
   Ⓑ unsureness
   Ⓒ inability

4. Which statement supports why the Red Cross Knight was *delighted?*
   Ⓐ An old hermit reminds him that he must face the dragon in the valley.
   Ⓑ The knight and Una accept the uncertainty of their futures.
   Ⓒ The knight sees a glorious palace on top of a mountain.

5. Chose the proper degrees of meaning for the word *dreadful.*
   Ⓐ wonderful – average – dreadful
   Ⓑ dreadful – terrible – gigantic
   Ⓒ outermost – innermost – dreadful

1. **debt**
(det) *n.*
money owed

2. **income**
(in´ kum´) *n.*
money taken in

3. **convenience**
(kən vēn´ yəns) *n.*
something that brings
ease

4. **bargain**
(bär´ gin) *n.*
sold cheaply

5. **asset**
(as´ et) *n.*
thing that has
cash value

6. **currency**
(kûr´ ən sē) *n.*
money or coins

7. **salesperson**
(sālz´ pûr´ sən) *n.*
someone who sells

8. **inexpensive**
(in´ ek spen´ siv) *adj.*
not costing much

9. **salary**
(sal´ ə rē) *n.*
payment for work

10. **loan**
(lōn) *n.*
something lent with
promise to return

# Dollars and Sense

## ① Word Meanings

## Cause and Effect

 Look at the cause-and-effect words in each sentence below to help you fill in the blank with the correct vocabulary word.

1. If you owe money to a person or an institution,

   you are in _____.

2. If you take out a_____, you must

   promise to pay it back within a certain amount of time.

3. A person with a high _____ can afford

   more because she is taking in a large amount of money.

4. If people would use only _____, they
   could spend only the money they had in their pockets.

5. Credit cards are a modern _____
   because they are easy to get, easy to use, and easy to carry.

6. Credit cards are _____ to get because
   it costs nothing to apply for them.

7. A car is an _____ because you can
   sell it for cash.

8. If a person cannot afford expensive things because of the

   _____ he receives for his work, he
   can still have fun shopping.

9. If you want to buy something for a low price,

   look for a _____.

10. Before a customer hands a _____ a
    credit card, he or she should think about only spending
    what money he or she actually has to stay out of debt.

## 2 Reference Skills

# Syllables

 Look up each vocabulary word in a dictionary or glossary. Write the word under the correct heading below according to the number of syllables it has. Draw a dot between each syllable.

**One Syllable**

_____

_____

_____

**Three Syllables**

_____

_____

_____

_____

**Two Syllables**

_____

_____

_____

**Four Syllables**

_____

_____

_____

_____

• • • • • • • • • • • • • • • • • • • • • • • • • • • • • • • • • • • • •

Read the passage below and circle the word breaks that are divided incorrectly. Write a correct division of the words you circled in the space provided.

My friend Eduardo is comparing the speed and conv- _____

_____ enience of buying books and music on the Internet to buying them

in the store. He finds that items advertised as inexpen- _____

_____ sive on Internet sites usually cost more when the price of

shipping is added. In the stores, Eduardo finds helpful sa- _____

_____ lespeople who show him items he wants at a barg- _____

_____ ain. Saving money, paying debts, and buying valuable asse- _____

_____ ts, such as a house will get Eduardo where he wants to be financially.

## Vocabulary List

1. debt
2. income
3. convenience
4. bargain
5. asset
6. currency
7. salesperson
8. inexpensive
9. salary
10. loan

# 3 Build New Vocabulary

## Singular and Plural Nouns

List singular and plural nouns under the correct heading below. (**Hint:** One of the vocabulary words is not a noun.)

| Singular | Plural |
|---|---|
| 1. _____ | debts |
| 2. income | _____ |
| 3. convenience | _____ |
| 4. bargain | _____ |
| 5. _____ | assets |
| 6. currency | _____ |
| 7. salesperson | _____ |
| 8. salary | _____ |
| 9. loan | _____ |

10. Which vocabulary word is not a noun?

_____

## Think About It

To form the plural of a hyphenated compound noun, make the most important part of the word plural. For example, one *brother-in-law* becomes two *brothers-in-law,* and a *half-truth* becomes two *half-truths.*

Score _____ (Top Score 10)

## Word Play

# Rhyming Riddles

 Answer each riddle below with a vocabulary word. The underlined words in the riddles are clues, and the words in the answers will rhyme.

1. What do you call the <u>salary</u> that a <u>baker</u> makes?

   crumb _____

2. What do you call the <u>money you owe</u> on a <u>swimming pool</u>?

   wet _____

3. What do you call money that a <u>dog</u> might <u>borrow</u>?

   bone _____

4. What do you call <u>money</u> you keep tucked away <u>for a crisis</u>?

   emergency _____

5. What do you call <u>vegetable seeds sold at a very low price</u>?

   garden _____

6. What do you call <u>money</u> that is very <u>easy to get</u>?

   dollars and cents _____

7. What do you call <u>things that have cash value</u> owned by <u>two people who sing together</u>?

   duets' _____

8. What do you call <u>someone who sells equipment</u> to <u>marine veterinarians</u>?

   whale surgeon _____

1. **professional**
(prə fesh´ ə nəl) *adj.*
businesslike manner

2. **industrious**
(in dus´ trē əs) *adj.*
hardworking

3. **dedicated**
(ded´ i kā´ təd) *adj.*
totally giving of
oneself

4. **promoted**
(prə mō´ təd) *v.*
raised in position

5. **earn**
(ûrn) *v.*
to receive in return for
work done

6. **ambition**
(am bish´ ən) *n.*
desire to achieve

7. **fire**
(fīr) *v.*
to dismiss from a job

8. **employ**
(em ploi´) *v.*
to give a job to

9. **intern**
(in´ tûrn) *n.*
person trained on the
job

10. **specialist**
(spesh´ ə list) *n.*
an expert

# Dreams to Jobs

## 1   Word Meanings

### Word Mapping

 Complete the chart by filling in the blanks with the words from the Word Bank below.

| Word Bank | | | | |
|---|---|---|---|---|
| lose | desire | professional | expert | hardworking |
| specialist | employ | dismiss | disloyal | advanced |

| Vocabulary Word | Synonym | Antonym |
|---|---|---|
| earn | gain | _____ |
| industrious | _____ | undisciplined |
| _____ | hire | fire |
| fire | _____ | hire |
| ambition | _____ | indifference |
| dedicated | loyal | _____ |
| intern | apprentice | _____ |
| promoted | _____ | demoted |
| _____ | expert | amateur |
| _____ | businesslike | informal |

• • • • • • • • • • • • • • • • • • • • • • • • • • • • • • • • • •

### ☀ Think About It

Many words have more than one synonym. For example, another synonym for *industrious* is *diligent*. Which vocabulary word is a synonym for *devoted?*

## 2  Reference Skills

# Phonetic Spellings

 Read each sentence below and decide which vocabulary word is represented by the phonetic spelling in parentheses. Write the vocabulary word in the blank.

1. George Washington Carver was a talented and

   (in dus´ trē əs) _____ scientist.

2. While he was seeking an education, people would (em ploi´)

   _____ Carver to cook and wash clothing.

3. Carver was known for his (prə fesh´ ə nəl)

   _____ attitude and his successful experiments with new plant products.

4. Carver's (am bish´ ən) _____ was to find new uses for common crops, such as peanuts.

5. For 47 years Carver was able to (ûrn)

   _____ a living at the Tuskegee Institute.

6. He was so (ded´ i kā´ təd) _____ to research that he left his life's savings to start the Carver Research Foundation.

• • • • • • • • • • • • • • • • • • • • • • • • • • • • • • • • • • • •

Look up the phonetic spelling for each word below and write it in the blank.

7. intern _____

8. specialist _____

9. fire _____

10. promoted _____

## Vocabulary List

1. professional
2. industrious
3. dedicated
4. promoted
5. earn
6. ambition
7. fire
8. employ
9. intern
10. specialist

 **3 Build New Vocabulary**

## Prefixes *un-* and *in-*

 Write the words from the box with the prefixes *un-* or *in-* next to their definitions.

| | | |
|---|---|---|
| unemployed | uncertain | inexpensive |
| unprofessional | unbearable | involuntary |

1. not sure _____

2. does not cost much _____

3. does not act in a polite, thoughtful, businesslike manner

   _____

4. not done by choice _____

5. not having a job _____

6. not able to be dealt with _____

• • • • • • • • • • • • • • • • • • • • • • • • • • • • • • • • • • • • • •

 Read each sentence below and circle *Correct* or *Incorrect*. Think about how the prefix affects the meaning of the word.

7. I was so happy to start my new job and finally be *unemployed*.　　Correct　　Incorrect

8. The trapped heat in our classroom was *unbearable*.　　Correct　　Incorrect

9. Cleaning my room today is not my choice; it is *involuntary*.　　Correct　　Incorrect

10. I made a good impression on my boss by acting *unprofessional*.　　Correct　　Incorrect

11. We were able to buy more of them because they were very *inexpensive*.　　Correct　　Incorrect

12. We thought he was sure because he said he was *uncertain*.　　Correct　　Incorrect

# 4 Word Play

## Stop-and-Think Questions

Read the questions below and write *Yes* or *No* to answer each. Then explain your answer.

1. Can I write vocabulary words onto my *specialist* at the back of my journal?

   _____

   _____

2. Are ants considered *industrious?*

   _____

   _____

3. Could a giraffe be *employed?*

   _____

   _____

4. To get to your house, would I need to *intern* at the stop sign?

   _____

   _____

5. If you were *promoted,* would you go to a higher grade in school?

   _____

   _____

6. Do you need *ambition* to sleep?

   _____

   _____

**1. reserved**
(ri zûrvd´) *adj.*
keeping feelings
to oneself

**2. generous**
(jen´ ər əs) *adj.*
willing to share

**3. charming**
(chär´ ming) *adj.*
delightful; pleasing

**4. stern**
(stûrn) *adj.*
firm; unmoving

**5. considerate**
(kən sid´ ər it) *adj.*
caring about others

**6. demanding**
(di man´ ding) *adj.*
needing much
attention

**7. sophisticated**
(sə fis´ ti kā´ tid) *adj.*
having worldly
experience

**8. sulky**
(sul´ kē) *adj.*
moody and quietly
angry

**9. enthusiastic**
(en thoo´ zē as´ tik)
*adj.* full of energy

**10. pessimistic**
(pes´ ə mis´ tik) adj.
expecting the worst

# Personality Traits

## 1 Word Meanings

## Extended Definitions

 Write the letter of the extended definition that belongs with each vocabulary word given.

1. _____ demanding

2. _____ stern

3. _____ enthusiastic

4. _____ sophisticated

5. _____ reserved

6. _____ charming

7. _____ pessimistic

8. _____ sulky

9. _____ considerate

10. _____ generous

**A.** having a lot of energy and lively interest

**B.** full of charm; fascinating, attractive, or delightful

**C.** having or showing a willingness to give or share freely

**D.** needing or insisting on much care, attention, time, or effort

**E.** in a gloomy, cross mood; quietly mad

**F.** not outgoing in manner; holding back

**G.** severe or strict, harsh; firm

**H.** having or showing respect for others and their feelings

**I.** having worldly knowledge and experience; more highly developed

**J.** expecting the worst or taking a negative view of life

 **Think About It**

When looking up a definition for an unfamiliar word, sometimes you will run into words in the definition that are also unfamiliar. By looking up those words, you can piece together a definition that makes sense to you.

Score _____ (Top Score 10)

## 2 Reference Skills

# Reference Tools

Read the sentences below and decide which reference book you would use. Choose among a rhyming dictionary, a thesaurus, or a dictionary.

1. One of the characters in your short story is *reserved.* You would like to use a different word that means the same thing as *reserved* to describe him. Where would you look?

   _____

2. You are creating a poem for the poetry contest and need a word that rhymes with the word *charming.* Where would

   you look? _____

3. In your silent-reading book about babysitting, you find the word *sulky* and do not know what it means.

   Where would you look? _____

4. You have already used the word *demanding* when writing a letter to your best friend. You want to find a synonym for *demanding.* Where would you look?

   _____

5. You are working on a crossword puzzle and your clue to the fifth word across is the past tense of *sophisticate.*

   Where would you look? _____

6. You are working on a songwriting project for music class. You and your partner cannot think of a word that rhymes with *considerate.*

   Where would you look? _____

## Vocabulary List

1. reserved
2. generous
3. charming
4. stern
5. considerate
6. demanding
7. sophisticated
8. sulky
9. enthusiastic
10. pessimistic

# 3 Build New Vocabulary

## Adjectives

 Read each sentence below that describes different kinds of people. Write the adjective from the Vocabulary List that could be used to describe each person.

1. Someone who is sensitive to how others feel is

   _____.

2. Someone who delights others with his or her pleasant

   personality is _____.

3. Someone who is quiet and restrained, or saves his or her

   comments, is _____.

4. Someone who gives commands and must have things his

   or her own way is _____.

5. Someone who has a great interest in and puts a lot of

   energy into something is _____.

6. Someone who freely shares what he or she has with

   others is _____.

7. Someone who sees the bad side in everything is

   _____.

8. Someone who has manners and worldly information from

   experience is _____.

9. Someone who is very strict and allows few exceptions to the

   rules is _____.

10. Someone who is stubbornly quiet because he or she is

   in a bad mood is_____.

# Word Play

## Who Knows?

 Read each description below. Choose the person from the box who best matches each description and write his or her name in the blank.

| | | |
|---|---|---|
| Demanding Dedra | Charming Charlie | Considerate Connie |
| Pessimistic Priscilla | Enthusiastic Eugene | Generous Giovanni |
| Sophisticated Sophia | Reserved Rosemary | Stern Stan |

1. He is invited to all parties because his compliments make everyone feel special. He's funny and fun to be around. He has never found a person that did not like him.

   _____

2. She thinks she should get everything she wants when she wants it. She is bossy and has trouble keeping friends because she requires so much attention.

   _____

3. You cannot tell if she is friendly or unfriendly because she rarely talks to others. She might be shy, but who can tell? She keeps her thoughts to herself.

   _____

4. He throws himself into every project he can, and he is very energetic. Sometimes other people cannot keep up with him.

   _____

5. She is always expecting the worst possible thing to happen. She is hardly ever cheery and positive.

   _____

**1. elegant**
(el´ i gənt) *adj.*
showing grace

**2. prosperous**
(pros´ pər əs) *adj.*
having success

**3. impressive**
(im pres´ iv) *adj.*
deserving of notice

**4. honor**
(on´ ərd) *v.*
to show respect for

**5. envy**
(en´ vē) *v.*
to be jealous of

**6. popularity**
(pop´ yə lar´ i tē) *n.*
state of being widely liked

**7. legendary**
(lej´ ən der´ ē) *adj.*
made famous through storytelling*

**8. praise**
(prāz) *n.*
words of admiration

**9. sensation**
(sen sā´ shən) *n.*
something that causes excitement

**10. celebrated**
(sel´ ə brā´ tid) *adj.*
famous

# "Fame & Wealth" Vocabulary

 **1** Word Meanings

## Examples and Nonexamples

 Read each description below. Write the letter of the missing example or nonexample that completes the description in the blank.

1. Elegant is a crystal chandelier and candlelight. Elegant is *not* _____.
   **a.** wearing a formal gown or tuxedo
   **b.** spilling your glass of milk at dinner

2. Legendary is Pocahontas. Legendary is *not* _____.
   **a.** Johnny Appleseed
   **b.** your new baby sister

3. Praise is _____. Praise is *not* "I see you are finally wearing a nice shirt."
   **a.** "I love your new shoes!"
   **b.** "Your lunch looks gross."

4. Celebrated is _____. Celebrated is *not* going unnoticed.
   **a.** having people ignore your work
   **b.** being recognized for what you have done

5. Envy is _____. Envy is *not* being proud of someone.
   **a.** wishing that you, instead of your friend, won first place
   **b.** encouraging others to do well

6. Impressive is learning ten new vocabulary words this week. Impressive is *not* _____.
   **a.** saying "I can't" without even trying
   **b.** learning to play a musical instrument

• • • • • • • • • • • • • • • • • • • • • • • • • • • • • • • • •

## Think About It

*A legend is a story passed down through the years about a person who may or may not be real. No one knows for sure if Robin Hood was a real person, but there are many legends about his adventures.

Score _____ (Top Score 6)          "Fame & Wealth" Vocabulary • **Word Meanings**

## 2 Reference Skills

# Multiple Meanings

Read the dictionary entries below. Then read the following sentences and choose the correct word and correct form of the word to complete each sentence. Finally, write the number of the definition you used.

**sensation** *n.* **1.** a person or thing that causes great excitement or interest: *an unbelievable sensation.* **2.** the process of feeling things by means of the senses: *the sensation of taste, the sensation of smell.* **3.** a feeling or impression coming from some particular situation: *When the light went out, I had a strong sensation of fear.*

**honor** *v.* **1.** to have high regard or esteem for; to show respect for: *A married person agrees to honor his or her spouse.* **2.** to accept as valid: *The store honored my coupon that had expired.*

**prosperous** *adj.* **1.** having wealth, success, or good fortune: *The industrial revolution was a prosperous time.* **2.** creating a favorable situation: *A prosperous wind brought the ships safely home.*

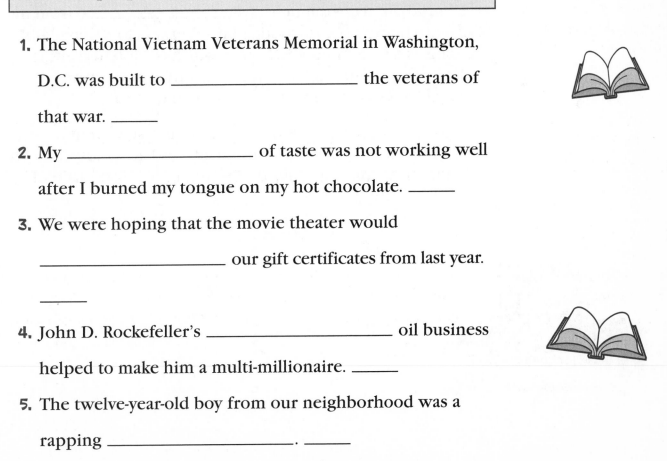

1. The National Vietnam Veterans Memorial in Washington, D.C. was built to _____ the veterans of that war. _____

2. My _____ of taste was not working well after I burned my tongue on my hot chocolate. _____

3. We were hoping that the movie theater would _____ our gift certificates from last year. _____

4. John D. Rockefeller's _____ oil business helped to make him a multi-millionaire. _____

5. The twelve-year-old boy from our neighborhood was a rapping _____ . _____

1. *elegant*

2. *prosperous*

3. *impressive*

4. *honor*

5. *envy*

6. *popularity*

7. *legendary*

8. *praise*

9. *sensation*

10. *celebrated*

## **3 Build New Vocabulary**

# Context Clues

Using the boldfaced context clues, fill in the blanks with the appropriate vocabulary words.

Henry Ford was a self-taught mechanic who moved to the city of Detroit at the age of 16 to work with steam engines. In his spare time, Ford starting building the Quadricycle, his first car. Some said it looked like a baby buggy with an engine. In

1901, his _____ new model beat the world's fastest automobile in a race; **it was worth noticing.** In 1903, Ford started his own car company.

By 1908 he built the famous Model T, also called the Tin Lizzie. This car was **liked by many** and quickly gained

_____. Automobiles were once something

that only _____ and **rich** families could enjoy, but **now they were affordable to the middle class.**

Henry Ford gained much _____ from his **admirers** because he introduced his workers to the assembly line. This is a system in which everyone has a job in making the finished product. Cars were being built **quicker and better than ever before,** which **caused** quite a

_____ in the world of industry. Henry Ford died at the age of 84 in 1947, but his life and accomplishments are honored at the Henry Ford Museum in his birthplace of Dearborn, Michigan.

# 4 Word Play

## Word Search

Find each of the vocabulary words in the word search puzzle. Words may be hidden across, down, or diagonally. (**Hint**: Each word touches another word.)

| A | K | L | B | R | I | O | Z | W | Y | T | J | K | L | R | U | O |
|---|---|---|---|---|---|---|---|---|---|---|---|---|---|---|---|---|
| B | D | N | Q | Y | S | R | A | T | B | C | F | L | I | G | M | H |
| N | I | L | G | C | H | T | I | W | H | X | U | X | W | U | L | T |
| J | F | O | B | E | P | R | O | S | P | E | R | O | U | S | E | T |
| M | D | K | M | Z | A | E | P | H | G | V | W | I | T | U | G | S |
| I | P | Y | O | L | J | D | H | S | F | H | O | N | O | R | E | D |
| R | M | A | U | M | L | A | F | E | U | P | Q | R | B | C | N | E |
| X | V | P | I | Q | N | C | E | L | E | B | R | A | T | E | D | S |
| N | O | B | R | Y | M | L | G | E | V | I | F | A | A | S | A | P |
| P | K | W | J | E | L | A | V | G | R | N | D | Y | I | Z | R | X |
| C | D | K | I | K | S | H | R | A | S | T | E | G | P | S | Y | R |
| F | Y | E | Z | G | J | S | E | N | S | A | T | I | O | N | E | K |
| D | Z | V | C | N | P | Q | I | T | P | N | O | J | R | O | T | Q |
| Q | A | O | L | B | Z | M | X | V | Y | O | B | S | W | U | C | W |
| B | D | F | H | J | L | O | P | S | E | N | V | Y | Z | A | N | R |

# Vocabulary for Time

**Vocabulary List**

1. **abruptly**
(ə brupt´ lē) *adv.*
suddenly

2. **subsequent**
(sub´ si kwənt) *adj.*
happening after

3. **frequent**
(frē´ kwənt) *adj.*
happening often

4. **ultimately**
(ul´ tə mit lē) *adv.*
in the end

5. **spontaneous**
(spon tā´ nē əs) *adj.*
not planned

6. **periodically**
(pir´ ē od´ ik lē) *adv.*
at regular times

7. **seldom**
(sel´ dəm) *adv.*
not often

8. **infinite**
(in´ fə nit) *adj.*
having no limits;
neverending

9. **synchronize**
(sing´ krə nīz´) *v.*
to make happen
at the same time

10. **session**
(sesh´ ən) *n.*
a period of time

## 1 Word Meanings

### Brainstorming

 Read each set of brainstormed ideas below. Choose the vocabulary word being described and write it in the blank.

1. happens at regular times—you can expect it

_____

2. has no limits—goes on forever _____

3. it means "suddenly"—it happens quickly

_____

4. happens at the end—it means "finally"

_____

5. happens once in a while—does not happen regularly

_____

6. set to happen at the same time as something else—done

together _____

7. comes after something—as a result of

_____

8. happens without planning—happens right away

_____

9. a specific amount of time—has a beginning and an end

_____

10. occurs often—happens again and again

_____

## ② Reference Skills

# Dictionary Entries

To look up a form of a word in a dictionary, you may need to look up the base word. Look at the dictionary entry below and answer the questions.

---

**a•brupt** (ə brupt′) *adj.* **1.** happening suddenly and without warning; unexpected: *I had to make an abrupt stop on my bike.* **2.** impolite; brusque: *Queenie is always abrupt when talking to her servants.* **3.** steep: *The plane made an abrupt climb.* [from Latin *abruptus* meaning "to break off" or "interrupt."] —**a•brupt′ ly** *adv.* —**a•brupt′ ness** *n.*

---

1. What base word would you need to look up to find

   *abruptly?* _____

2. What part of speech is *abrupt?* _____

3. How many definitions are given for *abrupt?* _____

4. Write the number of the definition that best fits *abrupt* as it is used in this sentence.
   There was an *abrupt* change in the weather yesterday.

   _____

5. How many syllables are in *abruptly?* _____

6. What part of speech is *abruptly?*

   _____

7. What other word form, in addition to *abruptly*, is given for

   *abrupt?* _____

8. Circle the letter of the sentence in which *abruptly* is used correctly.
   a. We abruptly waited for an hour before he arrived.
   b. After searching abruptly for a very long time, she found her lost dog.
   c. The teacher had to abruptly leave the classroom because she was having a baby.

## Vocabulary List

1. *abruptly*
2. *subsequent*
3. *frequent*
4. *ultimately*
5. *spontaneous*
6. *periodically*
7. *seldom*
8. *infinite*
9. *synchronize*
10. *session*

# 3 Build New Vocabulary

## Using the Suffix -ly

By adding the *-ly* ending to most adjectives, they become adverbs and can be used to describe verbs, adjectives, or other adverbs. Add *-ly* to the vocabulary word defined by the underlined words to complete each sentence below.

1. <u>Without making any plans</u>, he decided to go to the airport and _____ fly somewhere that would be warm and sunny.

2. _____, she would miss recess because her work was not done, a situation that <u>happened often</u>.

3. My chances are _____ better since there are <u>no limits</u> set on the number of votes.

4. I hope that <u>after</u> I take the science test, it will not _____ lower my grade.

· · · · · · · · · · · · · · · · · · · · · · · · · · · · · · · · · · · · · · · ·

Remove the *-ly* from the vocabulary word defined by the underlined words to complete each sentence below. (**Hint:** One of the vocabulary words is used twice.)

5. <u>In the end</u>, my _____ goal is to become a pediatrician.

6. <u>Without warning</u>, the narrow path took an _____ turn and descended down the side of the mountain.

7. <u>At regular times</u>, we hear the _____ cheers from the football fans.

8. The bus driver had to <u>quickly</u> react when she made an _____ stop to save the stray cat.

## Word Play

# Possible or Not Possible

 Read each sentence carefully and decide if it could or could not happen. If it is possible, circle P. If it is not possible, circle NP.

|  | **Possible** | **Not Possible** |
|---|---|---|
| 1. The flying jet stopped abruptly and gradually. | P | NP |
| 2. Ultimately, the decision was made by the principal. | P | NP |
| 3. The swimmers synchronized their routine. | P | NP |
| 4. The Cast family carefully planned a spontaneous vacation. | P | NP |
| 5. The baby cries frequently. | P | NP |
| 6. The time it takes to bake a loaf of bread is infinite. | P | NP |
| 7. The stoplight changes periodically. | P | NP |
| 8. The training session lasted all afternoon. | P | NP |
| 9. The flower died and subsequently bloomed. | P | NP |
| 10. The phone seldom rings in our classroom. | P | NP |

•••••••••••••••••••••••••••••••••••••••••••••••

 ## Think About It

Knowing a word and how to use it correctly can help you uncover false statements, solve riddles, and write jokes. Can you think of more impossible situations using the Vocabulary List words?

# Vocabulary Review

## ① Review Word Meanings

Read the passage below. Then answer the questions about the boldfaced vocabulary words.

## What Is Success?

Many children dream of growing up to become rich and famous. Singers, actors, athletes, politicians, writers, and captains of industry all enjoy **popularity** and **incomes** that some people **envy.** Imagine being **prosperous** enough to buy huge homes, expensive cars, and go on **spontaneous** vacations to **impressive** locations, such as the French Riviera, Tahiti, or Australia. Imagine creating a **sensation** when you step into a room, with cameras flashing and people **frequently** applauding because they recognize you.

Wouldn't it be fun to be such a **celebrated** and **honored** personality? With a lot of **ambition,** you may be able to reach such a goal. Of course, you must be completely **dedicated** to your career, but in the words of Ralph Waldo Emerson, "Nothing great was ever achieved without **enthusiasm.**"

Now read the following questions. Then completely fill in the bubble of the correct answer.

1. Which entry shows words you might brainstorm related to *popularity?*
   - Ⓐ happens after, following, next
   - Ⓑ stop, quick, ends
   - Ⓒ liked, known, celebrity

2. Which sentence uses cause-and-effect context clues to define *spontaneous* correctly?
   - Ⓐ Because their vacation was spontaneous, they had no plan other than to head west.
   - Ⓑ They took a spontaneous and elegant vacation.
   - Ⓒ They took a spontaneous, planned vacation.

3. Which word with the suffix *-ly* is defined as "happening often"?
   - Ⓐ ultimately
   - Ⓑ frequently
   - Ⓒ elegantly

4. What is the definition of *prosperous?*
   - Ⓐ having success and wealth
   - Ⓑ having many friends
   - Ⓒ being well-known

5. If someone shows enthusiasm, he or she is _____.
   - Ⓐ enthusiast
   - Ⓑ enthuse
   - Ⓒ enthusiastic

## ② Review Word Meanings

Read the passage below. Then answer the questions about the boldfaced vocabulary words.

# Making a Living

Have you given any thought to how you would like to **earn** a living when you grow up? There are so many careers that it seems as though there is an **infinite** number of choices. Even though there are many different kinds of jobs, you must be **industrious** to find the best one for you.

First, you must be qualified and **professional.** Depending on the job, that may mean that you need to have the right education, the right experience, or the right attitude. Then you must know what you want. Is a big **salary** important to you? Or perhaps getting **promoted** to a high position is more important. Perhaps you would like to work with people. Maybe being a **salesperson** is right for you. Whatever career you **ultimately** choose, the people or company that **employs** you will **praise** and reward you if you are dedicated to your work. If you are not, they may be **firing** you before you know it.

Now read the following questions. Then completely fill in the bubble of the correct answer.

1. Which word is a form of *ultimate?*
   - Ⓐ employ
   - Ⓑ infinite
   - Ⓒ ultimately

2. Which word means "boundless or neverending"?
   - Ⓐ infinite
   - Ⓑ industrious
   - Ⓒ promoted

3. Onto which word can *un-* be added to make a word that means the same as *firing?*
   - Ⓐ praise
   - Ⓑ employ
   - Ⓒ professional

4. For which word is (sal′ ə rē) the phonetic spelling?
   - Ⓐ salary
   - Ⓑ salesperson
   - Ⓒ centered

5. Which sentence uses cause-and-effect context clues to define *promoted* correctly?
   - Ⓐ Ishmael worked hard, acted professionally, and as a result was promoted.
   - Ⓑ Ishmael promoted more than anyone else in the department.
   - Ⓒ Ishmael was promoted last month to head supervisor.

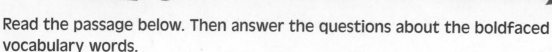

## Review Word Meanings

Read the passage below. Then answer the questions about the boldfaced vocabulary words.

## Money Sense

What will you do with the money you earn? Have you ever heard the expression "A fool and his money are soon parted"? Will you be like the fool and his money? Perhaps you will spend more than you have in **currency,** buying every **convenience** you see, and need **subsequent loans** to pay off your **debts.** Or maybe you will live by the saying "A penny saved is a penny earned." You could look for **bargains,** such as **inexpensive** or on-sale items that you need, and only **periodically** buy a convenience, such as a microwave. Or will you be a **generous** spirit, one who follows the Persian saying "I complained that I had no shoes until I met a man who had no feet?" Will you donate your **assets** to organizations that help those who have less than you do?

Now read the following questions. Then completely fill in the bubble of the correct answer.

1. Which word is an antonym for *expensive?*
   - Ⓐ generous
   - Ⓑ bargains
   - Ⓒ inexpensive

2. Which of the following is not an example of *generous?*
   - Ⓐ giving food to a food pantry
   - Ⓑ keeping all of your money, time, and talents to yourself
   - Ⓒ offering to share part of your lunch

3. Which word means "money that has to be paid back"?
   - Ⓐ assets
   - Ⓑ convenience
   - Ⓒ loans

4. Which word is a synonym for *money?*
   - Ⓐ bargains
   - Ⓑ currency
   - Ⓒ subsequent

5. To which of the following words could you add the suffix *-ly?*
   - Ⓐ subsequent
   - Ⓑ bargain
   - Ⓒ convenience

 **Review Word Meanings**

Read the passage below. Then answer the questions about the boldfaced vocabulary words.

# Rich in Friends

Success is not just measured by the salary you earn or how you choose to use that income. Success is also measured by one's friends. After all, there is the saying "Make new friends, but keep the old. One is silver, the other gold." If you are kind, **charming,** and **considerate,** nearly everyone you meet will want to be your friend. You will **seldom** be alone if you are **elegant** and **sophisticated.**

You can also have friends if you are **reserved,** but they will have to understand your desire for privacy. It may be a little harder to make friends if you are **stern.** People may not think you know how to have fun, but they will just have to give you a chance. You may have a difficult time making friends if you are **sulky** because this makes people uncomfortable; if you are **demanding,** you may find friendship after friendship ending **abruptly.** Do not give up, though, because there is always someone out there who will understand you. When you do make friends, however, you should always remember to treat others the way you want to be treated.

Now read the following questions. Then completely fill in the bubble of the correct answer.

1. If you wanted to look up the definition for *stern,* where would you look?
   Ⓐ dictionary
   Ⓑ thesaurus
   Ⓒ atlas

2. Which of the following is a synonym for *sulky?*
   Ⓐ happy
   Ⓑ moody
   Ⓒ anxious

3. Which of the following is not an example of *charming?*
   Ⓐ a well-liked person
   Ⓑ an attractive house
   Ⓒ a toddler throwing a temper tantrum

4. Which word below has four syllables?
   Ⓐ sophisticated
   Ⓑ reserved
   Ⓒ considerate

5. Which meaning of *stern* is used in the passage above?
   Ⓐ the rear part of the boat
   Ⓑ severe or strict
   Ⓒ gloomy

**1. physician**
(fə zish´ ən) *n.*
medical doctor

**2. recuperate**
(ri ko͞o´ pə rāt´) *v.*
to gain back health

**3. cure**
(kyo͞or) *v.*
to make well

**4. condition**
(kən dish´ ən) *n.*
a disease or ailment

**5. surgeon**
(sûr´ jən) *n.*
a medical doctor
who operates

**6. infection**
(in fek´ shən) *n.*
a disease caused by
germs

**7. fatal**
(fā´ təl) *adj.*
resulting in death

**8. treatment**
(trēt´ mənt) *n.*
plan for treating
sickness

**9. microscopic**
(mī´ krə skop´ ik) *adj.*
extremely small

**10. bandage**
(ban´ dij) *n.*
material to cover
wound

# From Mystery to Medicine

## ① Word Meanings

### Semantic Web

 Complete the word web below by writing each
vocabulary word where it best fits.

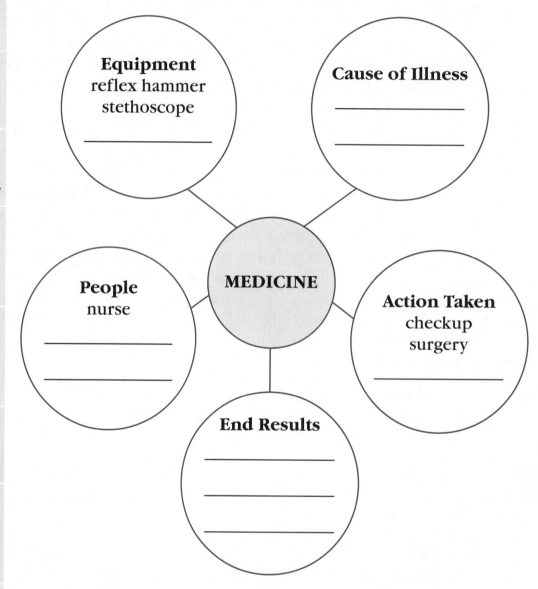

Equipment
reflex hammer
stethoscope
_____

Cause of Illness
_____
_____

People
nurse
_____
_____

MEDICINE

Action Taken
checkup
surgery
_____

End Results
_____
_____
_____

• • • • • • • • • • • • • • • • • • • • • • • • • • • • • • • • • • • • • •

 What vocabulary word is defined as too small to
be seen by the unaided eye but large enough to be
studied under a microscope?

_____

**2** **Reference Skills**

## Using a Glossary

 Fill in the missing words from the Vocabulary List in alphabetical order. Then, using the glossary, circle the number of syllables in each word. Finally place a check mark next to its part or parts of speech.

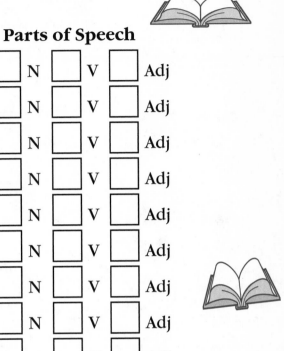

| Vocabulary Word | Number of Syllables | Parts of Speech |
|---|---|---|
| 1. bandage | 1 2 3 4 | ☐ N ☐ V ☐ Adj |
| 2. _____ | 1 2 3 4 | ☐ N ☐ V ☐ Adj |
| 3. _____ | 1 2 3 4 | ☐ N ☐ V ☐ Adj |
| 4. fatal | 1 2 3 4 | ☐ N ☐ V ☐ Adj |
| 5. infection | 1 2 3 4 | ☐ N ☐ V ☐ Adj |
| 6. _____ | 1 2 3 4 | ☐ N ☐ V ☐ Adj |
| 7. physician | 1 2 3 4 | ☐ N ☐ V ☐ Adj |
| 8. _____ | 1 2 3 4 | ☐ N ☐ V ☐ Adj |
| 9. _____ | 1 2 3 4 | ☐ N ☐ V ☐ Adj |
| 10. treatment | 1 2 3 4 | ☐ N ☐ V ☐ Adj |

• • • • • • • • • • • • • • • • • • • • • • • • • • • • • • • • • •

 Match each vocabulary word below with its definition.

11. _____ cure

**A.** material used in covering or binding a wound

12. _____ infection

**B.** a disease caused by harmful bacteria or viruses

13. _____ microscopic

**C.** too small to be seen with the human eye

14. _____ physician

**D.** to return to a healthy condition

15. _____ bandage

**E.** causing death

16. _____ fatal

**F.** a medical doctor

## Vocabulary List

1. *physician*

2. *recuperate*

3. *cure*

4. *condition*

5. *surgeon*

6. *infection*

7. *fatal*

8. *treatment*

9. *microscopic*

10. *bandage*

# 3 Build New Vocabulary

## Prefixes and Suffixes

Write the vocabulary word and the words from the box below that contain each prefix or suffix.

| American | microphone | development | microwave |
|----------|------------|-------------|-----------|
| emotion | veteran | judgment | |

| Prefix/Suffix | Meaning | Words |
|---------------|---------|-------|
| 1. *micro-* | small; short | _____ |
| | | _____ |
| | | _____ |
| 2. *-ment* | action | _____ |
| | | _____ |
| | | _____ |
| 3. *-an* | relating to | _____ |
| | | _____ |
| | | _____ |
| 4. *-ion* | state of | _____ |
| | | _____ |
| | | _____ |

Score _____ (Top Score 12)   From Mystery to Medicine • Build New Vocabulary

## Word Play

# Word Flowchart

 The chart below traces the actions you might take if you are ill. Complete the chart using the vocabulary words.

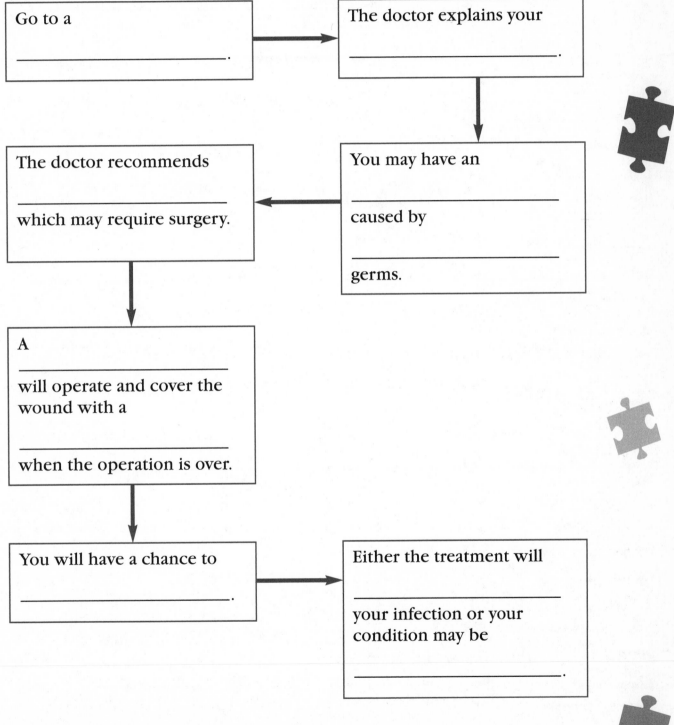

Go to a

_____ .

The doctor explains your

_____ .

The doctor recommends

_____

which may require surgery.

You may have an

_____

caused by

_____

germs.

A

_____

will operate and cover the
wound with a

_____

when the operation is over.

You will have a chance to

_____ .

Either the treatment will

_____

your infection or your
condition may be

_____ .

1. **progression**
(prə gresh´ ən) *n.*
moving ahead

2. **admission**
(ad mish´ ən) *n.*
fee to enter

3. **destination**
(des´ tə nā´ shən) *n.*
where one is going

4. **competition**
(kom´ pi tish´ ən) *n.*
a contest

5. **tension**
(ten´ shən) *n.*
nervous strain

6. **appreciation**
(ə prē´ shē ā´ shən)
*n.* thankfulness

7. **completion**
(kəm plē´ shən) *n.*
act of finishing

8. **friction**
(frik´ shən) *n.*
result of objects
rubbed together

9. **invitation**
(in´ vi tā´ shən) *n.*
asking someone's
presence

10. **plantation**
(plan tā´ shən) *n.*
a large single-crop
farm

# Nouns Ending in -ion

## 1 Word Meanings

### Analogies

 Read the analogies below. Decide which vocabulary word best completes each analogy and write it in the blank.

1. *door* is to *closed* as *homework* is to _____

2. *run* is to *home plate* as *travel* is to
_____

3. *ticket* is to *movie* as _____ is to *party*

4. *key* is to *unlock* as _____ is to *entering*

5. *cow* is to *farm* as *corn* is to _____

6. *calm* is to *stress* as *relaxation* is to _____

7. *backward* is to *regression* as *forward* is to
_____

8. *kindness* is to *friendliness* as *thankfulness* is to
_____

9. *germ* is to *illness* as _____ is to *fire*

10. *open* is to *seal* as *cooperation* is to _____

### Think About It

When solving analogies, it is important to think about the "bridge" between the two known words and then apply it to the missing word. You can use analogies to describe something. You might say a *cocoon* is to a *caterpillar* as an *egg* is to a *chicken*.

## ② Reference Skills

# Using a Glossary

 Choose the vocabulary word that best matches each definition below. Circle the letter of the correct answer.

**1.** a. temptation : a large southern farm
b. plantation

**2.** a. progression : the act of progressing or moving
b. destination  ahead

**3.** a. appreciation : the act of finishing
b. completion

**4.** a. expiration : a place where something or someone
b. destination  is going

**5.** a. animation : the rubbing of one item over another
b. friction

**6.** a. invitation : the act of inviting
b. sensation

**7.** a. admission : the act of being grateful
b. appreciation

**8.** a. competition : a contest or a struggle
b. prediction

**9.** a. tension : mental or emotional strain or stress
b. elevation

**10.** a. opinion : the payment needed to enter
b. admission

## Vocabulary List

1. progression
2. admission
3. destination
4. competition
5. tension
6. appreciation
7. completion
8. friction
9. invitation
10. plantation

# 3 Build New Vocabulary

## Words with -ion

All of the vocabulary words in this lesson end in the suffix -ion. Look at each base word below and write the vocabulary word that matches. Be sure to check your spelling.

1. progress _____

2. invite _____

3. tense _____

4. destine _____

5. complete _____

6. compete _____

7. admit _____

8. appreciate _____

Use the vocabulary words from above to complete the following sentences.

9. I always show my _____ by writing thank-you notes.

10. After paying the _____, our hands were stamped and we entered the state fair.

11. The tornado chasers tracked the _____ of the storm through the area.

12. When we arrived at our _____, we were happy to stretch our legs after riding in the cramped car for so long.

Score _____ (Top Score 12)   Nouns Ending in -ion • Build New Vocabulary

# 4  Word Play

## Words Within Words

The underlined words in the sentences below can be made from some of the letters in the vocabulary words. Read each sentence and the underlined words carefully. Choose the best vocabulary word to complete each sentence.

1. The <u>pilot</u> flew over the <u>plantain</u> _____.

2. At the _____ of the <u>moonlit</u> flight, the <u>copilot</u> landed the plane.

3. The important <u>tennis</u> match filled her with anxiety and _____.

4. The _____ of the newspaper's early <u>edition</u> was the front porch.

5. The <u>erosion's</u> _____ threatened the shoreline.

6. The newscaster's <u>reaction</u> to the much needed <u>raincoat</u> was _____.

7. The president gave an _____ to the <u>nation</u> to join in singing the "Star-Spangled Banner."

8. The science of _____ is not <u>fiction</u>.

9. Her <u>mission</u> was to <u>add</u> up the coins in the piggy bank to pay their _____ to the movie.

10. He won the _____ with his <u>poem</u> about his <u>pet</u> kitten named <u>Mitten</u>.

**Vocabulary List**

1. **synthetic**
   (sin thet´ ik) *adj.*
   made by humans

2. **textile**
   (teks´ tĭl) *n.*
   woven cloth

3. **velvet**
   (vel´ vit) *n.*
   cloth with smooth,
   thick fibers

4. **canvas**
   (kan´ vəs) *n.*
   strong, heavy cloth

5. **enamel**
   (i nam´ əl) *n.*
   hard, glossy coating

6. **slate**
   (slāt) *n.*
   bluish-gray rock

7. **aluminum**
   (ə lōō´ mə nəm) *n.*
   silver metal

8. **texture**
   (teks´ chər) *n.*
   look or feel of
   woven fabric

9. **adobe**
   (ə dō´ bē) *n.*
   sun-dried clay brick

10. **granite**
    (gran´ it) *n.*
    hard quartz rock
    made by heat

# Vocabulary for Materials

**1** **Word Meanings**

## Classifying

Four of the vocabulary words are related only to cloth and five are not. One vocabulary word relates to both. Using the vocabulary words and their definitions, write each under the best heading below.

| **Cloth** | **Not Cloth** |
|-----------|---------------|
| _____ | _____ |
| _____ | _____ |
| _____ | _____ |
| _____ | _____ |
| _____ | _____ |
|  | _____ |

Now using the vocabulary words under **Not Cloth** and their definitions, classify them as elements that come from Earth and those that do not. If necessary, look in a dictionary for help.

| **From Earth** | **Not From Earth** |
|----------------|--------------------|
| _____ | _____ |
| _____ | _____ |
| _____ |  |

Which vocabulary word is defined as something made artificially and does not occur naturally?

_____

Score _____ (Top Score 18)          Vocabulary for Materials • Word Meanings

## 2 — Reference Skills

# Using a Dictionary

 Read each dictionary entry below. Write the definition that best matches the boldfaced word and fits the context of the sentence.

> **e•nam•el** (i nam′ əl) *n.* **1.** hard, glossy substance covering metal or pottery **2.** paint that dries to a hard, glossy finish **3.** hard, glossy substance which covers the outside of the teeth

**1.** The dentist said sugar was ruining my **enamel.**

_____

_____

**2.** I chose a hot pink **enamel** for my wooden dresser drawers.

_____

_____

> **slate** (slāt) *n.* **1.** a bluish-gray rock that easily splits into thin layers **2.** a small writing tablet **3.** a record of someone's past performance **4.** a dull, dark bluish-gray color

**3.** Jeremiah could not wipe the chalk off his **slate.**

_____

_____

**4.** The artist chose the **slate** pastel for the stormy looking sky in her newest picture.

_____

_____

**5.** The chalkboard in the old schoolhouse was made of **slate.**

_____

_____

## Vocabulary List

1. synthetic
2. textile
3. velvet
4. canvas
5. enamel
6. slate
7. aluminum
8. texture
9. adobe
10. granite

# 3 Build New Vocabulary

## Root Words

 Write the vocabulary words and the words from the box below that contain each root.

| destruction | sympathy | finally |
| paragraph | infinite | century |

| Root | Meaning | Words Containing Root |
|---|---|---|
| 1. cent | one hundred | _____ |
| 2. struct | build | _____ |
| 3. fin | end or limit | _____ |
|  |  | _____ |
| 4. pathy | feeling | _____ |
| 5. tex | weave | _____ |
|  |  | _____ |
| 6. graph | write | _____ |

• • • • • • • • • • • • • • • • • • • • • • • • • • • • • • • • • • •

 Match the following vocabulary words with their definitions.

7. _____ slate     **A.** sun-dried, clay brick

8. _____ synthetic     **B.** silver metal from Earth's crust

9. _____ adobe     **C.** bluish-gray rock

10. _____ enamel     **D.** hard quartz rock made by heat

11. _____ granite     **E.** hard, glossy coating

12. _____ aluminum     **F.** made by humans; not natural

# 4 Word Play

## Give an Example

For each vocabulary word below, place a check mark next to examples of or things made from it.

1. synthetic ☐ nylon ☐ polyester ☐ cotton

2. textile ☐ cotton ☐ plastic ☐ wool

3. velvet ☐ ribbon ☐ curtains ☐ paper

4. canvas ☐ backpack ☐ computer ☐ surface used for oil painting

5. enamel ☐ paint ☐ coating of a vase ☐ coating of teeth

6. slate ☐ roofs ☐ chalkboards ☐ ice cream cone

7. aluminum ☐ cookies ☐ foil ☐ pans

8. texture ☐ bumpy ☐ smooth ☐ prickly

9. adobe ☐ pottery ☐ telephone ☐ bricks

10. granite ☐ birthday cakes ☐ statues ☐ buildings

• • • • • • • • • • • • • • • • • • • • • • • • • • • • • • • • • •

Read the following clues and pay attention to the boldfaced words. Write the vocabulary word related to each boldfaced word in the blank.

11. Please do not scratch your **name** into this. _____

12. You will find this in Braille **text.** _____

13. The statue captured his figure as he **ran.** _____

14. **Do be** careful of those hot bricks. _____

15. The last **can** of juice is in the backpack. _____

16. **The** material is fake. _____

**Vocabulary List**

1. **auditorium**
(ô′ di tôr′ ē əm) *n.*
public meeting room

2. **balcony**
(bal′ kə nē) *n.*
the upper floor
of auditorium

3. **orchestra**
(or′ kə strə) *n.*
a group of musicians

4. **classic**
(klas′ ik) *adj.*
of high quality

5. **high-pitched**
(hī′ picht′) *adj.*
having a shrill sound

6. **masterpiece**
(mas′ tər pēs′) *n.*
a great work

7. **academy**
(ə kad′ ə mē) *n.*
school with a focus

8. **rehearsal**
(ri hûr′ səl) *n.*
a practice before a
performance

9. **scene**
(sēn) *n.*
the place and time
of a play

10. **dramatic**
(drə mat′ ik) *adj.*
an emotional effect

# "Performance" Vocabulary

**1** **Word Meanings**

## What is Defined?

 Read the following definitions. Then write the
vocabulary word being defined in the blank.

1. Place and time: the setting of the play

   _____

2. Emotional impact is caused: striking and exciting

   _____

3. Refers to a high, shrill sound _____

4. Floor above others in an auditorium

   _____

5. Of higher quality: serves as a standard or guide

   _____

6. Running through a practice before the performance

   _____

7. Meeting room for large, public gatherings

   _____

8. Institution that focuses on a specific area of study

   _____

9. Not an ordinary piece of work: made with supreme skill

   _____

10. Group of musicians playing together on various
    instruments

    _____

## ② Reference Skills

### Syllables

 Look up each word below in the dictionary or glossary. Then circle the letter of the answer that shows the correct division for each word.

1. auditorium   **a.** au•di•to•ri•um   **b.** aud•it•or•i•um   **c.** au•dit•ori•um

2. balcony   **a.** balc•ony   **b.** bal•co•ny   **c.** balco•ny

3. orchestra   **a.** or•ches•tra   **b.** or•chest•ra   **c.** o•rch•es•t•ra

4. classic   **a.** cl•as•sic   **b.** class•ic   **c.** clas•sic

5. high-pitched   **a.** hi•gh-pit•ched   **b.** high-pitched   **c.** high-pit•ched

6. masterpiece   **a.** mas•ter•piece   **b.** ma•ster•piece   **c.** mast•er•piece

7. academy   **a.** ac•ad•em•y   **b.** a•cad•e•my   **c.** acad•emy

8. rehearsal   **a.** re•hears•al   **b.** re•hear•sal   **c.** reh•ears•al

9. scene   **a.** sce•ne   **b.** scene   **c.** sc•en•e

10. dramatic   **a.** dramat•ic   **b.** dra•mat•ic   **c.** dram•a•tic

 **Think About It**

When breaking words into syllables, you will find that a consonant between two vowels usually travels with the second vowel; for example, dra•ma and mu•sic.

## Vocabulary List

1. auditorium
2. balcony
3. orchestra
4. classic
5. high-pitched
6. masterpiece
7. academy
8. rehearsal
9. scene
10. dramatic

# 3 Build New Vocabulary

## Context Clues

Use the underlined context clues to write the best vocabulary word to complete each sentence below.

1. The Juilliard <u>School</u> in New York City is a well-known _____ for the performing arts.

2. Students are taught to <u>play instruments</u> so that they might one day be in an _____.

3. Students who sing must learn to hear and imitate <u>low-pitched</u> notes <u>as well as</u> _____ ones.

4. Students may also choose to learn to perform _____ parts in plays that may require many <u>emotions</u>.

5. _____ is a big part of <u>practicing</u> to get better.

6. For one play, they learn their lines and help <u>set</u> up a _____ on the stage.

7. Many hours are spent <u>on the stage</u> in the _____ going over the play.

8. It takes a lot of work to perform a _____, or <u>high-quality</u>, play.

9. So the next time you watch a wonderful performance <u>from high above</u> in the _____, remember that a lot of work and training went into it.

10. Some people say a good performance is a _____ <u>just like a beautiful painting</u> is.

## 4 Word Play

# Can You Picture It?

 Write the vocabulary word shown by each picture below.

1.

_____

4.

_____

2.

_____

5.

_____

3.

_____

6.

_____

• • • • • • • • • • • • • • • • • • • • • • • • • • • • • • • • • • • • • • • • • • • • •

Now draw pictures for the labels below.

7. auditorium

8. rehearsal

"Performance" Vocabulary • Word Play          Score _____ (Top Score 8)      Unit 3 • Lesson 16      **65**

# "Light and Color" Vocabulary

## 1 Word Meanings

### Finding Definitions

**1. variation**
(vâr´ ē ā´ shən) *n.*
amount of difference

**2. flash**
(flash) *n.*
a quick burst of light

**3. transparent**
(trans pâr´ ənt) *adj.*
easily seen through

**4. brilliant**
(bril´ yənt) *adj.*
shining brightly

**5. indigo**
(in´ di gō´) *n.*
a deep blue color

**6. shade**
(shād) *v.*
to darken

**7. crimson**
(krim´ zən) *n.*
a deep red color

**8. tinge**
(tinj) *v.*
to add a little color to

**9. ivory**
(ī´ və rē) *n.*
a creamy white color

**10. prism**
(priz´ əm) *n.*
bends light rays

 Use the underlined definition to find the best vocabulary word to complete each sentence below.

1. A _____ is a triangular-shaped piece of glass used to <u>bend white light rays</u>.

2. Shining light from a flashlight looks like a soft

   _____ color, <u>rich and creamy white</u>, but is actually a mix of many colors.

3. <u>Shining a bright light</u> on a prism will result in a

   _____ rainbow of colors.

4. A prism must be _____ and <u>easily seen through</u> to work properly.

5. The rainbow that appears from the prism always appears in the same order from a <u>deep red color</u>, known as

   _____, to violet.

6. You will notice that little _____ occurs <u>between each color as it changes</u>.

7. Sometimes the sun will _____ from behind the clouds <u>to shine quickly and brightly</u> on the rainy sky and a rainbow will appear.

8. Prisms teach us that raindrops in the air bend the light

   and _____ the sky <u>with a little color</u>.

9. You will find the color _____ if you look closely between the <u>blue</u> and violet bands.

10. If you see the clouds begin to <u>darken</u> and

    _____ the sky and you feel rain falling, look for a little sun and nature's most beautiful gifts of color, the rainbow.

## ② Reference Skills

# Multiple Meanings

 Decide which meaning of *brilliant* is used in each sentence below. Then write the number of the definition in the box.

> **brilliant** *adj.* **1.** bright, shining, gleaming, sparkling, twinkling, vivid **2.** clever, very intelligent, talented, gifted

1. ☐ Polaris is a *brilliant* star.

2. ☐ A diamond is a *brilliant* gem.

3. ☐ Albert Einstein was a *brilliant* scientist born late in the nineteenth century.

4. ☐ *Brilliant* fireworks exploded in the night sky.

5. ☐ Thomas Edison was a *brilliant* inventor who received most of his education from his mother.

Decide which meaning of *shade* is used in each sentence below. Then write the number of the definition in the box.

> **shade** *n.* **1.** darkness caused by something that cuts off light **2.** something that is used to reduce light *v.* **3.** to darken

6. ☐ My art teacher asked me to *shade* the circles in my drawing.

7. ☐ The old, lazy dog was lying in the *shade* all afternoon.

8. ☐ We were surprised to find that our new lamp did not come with a *shade*.

9. ☐ Our eyes had to adjust to the sun after sitting in the *shade*.

10. ☐ We added a drop of black paint to *shade* the bright blue to indigo.

## Vocabulary List

1. *variation*
2. *flash*
3. *transparent*
4. *brilliant*
5. *indigo*
6. *shade*
7. *crimson*
8. *tinge*
9. *ivory*
10. *prism*

# 3 Build New Vocabulary

## Context Clues

Write the vocabulary word in the blank that best completes each item below.

1. One saying goes: Variety is the spice of life.

   A _____ of this saying would be: Difference is what makes life exciting.

2. Sometimes people have bad reasons for doing something when they say they are doing it for a good reason. Sometimes it is easy to figure out or see through to the real reason. You might say this person is so

   _____.

3. The keys on a piano are black and white. Many years ago, the white keys were made from tusks. That is why when someone is playing the piano you might say he or she is

   tickling the _____.

4. Someone who is angry or embarrassed might turn red. Someone who is very angry or embarrassed might turn

   _____.

5. This word means "bright". The sun, students, and good moves in a checker game can all be called

   _____.

  **Word Play**

## Similes

Complete each simile below with the vocabulary word that best fits.

1. as _____ as a beet

2. as _____ as glass

3. as _____ as a diamond

4. came and left as fast as a _____

5. the _____ was extreme, like night and day

6. the _____ cast beautiful colors across the room like an artist painting with light

• • • • • • • • • • • • • • • • • • • • • • • • • • • • • • • • • •

Match the following vocabulary words with their definitions.

7. shade _____        **A.** a deep blue color

8. ivory _____        **B.** to darken

9. tinge _____        **C.** a creamy white color

10. indigo _____       **D.** to add a little color to

# Vocabulary Review

## 1 Review Word Meanings

Read the passage below. Then answer the questions about the boldfaced vocabulary words.

## Colonial Medicine

Life in our country 200 years ago was not easy, especially for those who were sick. The illnesses people suffered were awful, but the steps taken in order to be **cured** were often as bad, or worse. Whether you lived in the Ohio wilderness or on a Georgia **plantation,** you probably would not see a **physician** for most conditions. There were not many doctors and those available were very expensive. Women treated most problems with home remedies such as herbs, honey, snail water, flowers, and berries.

If you had a bad tooth, a barber/**surgeon** would take a break from cutting hair to pull the tooth, without giving you anything for the pain. For very serious conditions, a physician may have come to look at you. At the **completion** of the exam, he would bleed you, either by cutting you or putting leeches on your skin to suck out the bad blood. Reading about the medical practices of 200 years ago will help you gain **appreciation** for the way things are today. Physicians are well trained and many treatments are available, including **synthetic** medicines.

Now read the following questions. Then completely fill in the bubble of the correct answer.

1. Which of the following is a synonym for *cured?*
   - Ⓐ treated
   - Ⓑ healed
   - Ⓒ examined

2. You can show your appreciation, or _____, by being a good patient.
   - Ⓐ caring
   - Ⓑ displeasure
   - Ⓒ thankfulness

3. Herbs are used as natural medicines. Synthetic medicines are made by _____ .
   - Ⓐ humans
   - Ⓑ changes in the weather
   - Ⓒ hospitals

4. *Beginning* is to *start* as _____ is to *end*.
   - Ⓐ *treatment*
   - Ⓑ *appreciation*
   - Ⓒ *completion*

5. My _____ told me to get more exercise and eat more fruits and vegetables.
   - Ⓐ physician
   - Ⓑ plantation
   - Ⓒ treatment

## ② Review Word Meanings

Read the passage below. Then answer the questions about the boldfaced vocabulary words.

# Marie Curie

Marie Curie was a scientist who was born in 1867. Her admission to Sorbonne, a well-known college in Paris, France, enabled her to meet Pierre Curie, who later became her husband. Marie and Pierre discovered that the natural material radium was radioactive, which meant that it gave off energy. Because of Marie and Pierre's **classic** research, radium was used in the **treatment** of tumors.

Marie Curie's work with radioactive materials also helped in the development of X-rays. She made America her **destination** when she received an **invitation** to travel to America to receive the gift of an expensive gram of radium to use in her research. Unfortunately, Marie developed a **fatal condition** caused by her work with radioactive materials. She died in 1934.

Now read the following questions. Then completely fill in the bubble of the correct answer.

1. Which meaning of *condition* is used in the passage above?
   Ⓐ fee used to enter
   Ⓑ agreeing as truth
   Ⓒ a disease

2. What is the meaning of *classic* in the following sentence?
   *Marie Curie's classic studies of radium are still respected.*
   Ⓐ an emotional effect
   Ⓑ very rich in color, vivid
   Ⓒ seen as a standard of quality; of lasting value

3. What word tells you that Marie Curie's illness would lead to her death?
   Ⓐ fatal
   Ⓑ treatment
   Ⓒ condition

4. Some events are so special that no one can attend without an _____.
   Ⓐ treatment
   Ⓑ invitation
   Ⓒ condition

5. _____ may lead to a cure.
   Ⓐ Treatment
   Ⓑ Invitation
   Ⓒ Condition

6. In which choice is the word *invitation* correctly divided into syllables?
   Ⓐ invi•ta•tion
   Ⓑ in•vit•ation
   Ⓒ in•vi•ta•tion

# ③ Review Word Meanings

Read the passage below. Then answer the questions about the boldfaced vocabulary words.

## Joseph Lister

Joseph Lister was responsible for an important medical discovery in the 1800s. He found that many people did not **recuperate** after their surgery. In fact they often died from gangrene, an **infection** they picked up during the surgery. Due to the **progression** of gangrene, some patients had to have limbs removed in order to save their lives.

Unfortunately this did not always work. Lister decided to experiment. He knew about **microscopic** germs, and he knew that carbolic acid was used to clean drains. He put carbolic acid on a **bandage** before he covered a wound on an eleven-year-old patient, and an infection did not develop. After this discovery, operating rooms were kept clean, surgeons wore clean clothes, and instruments were disinfected with a spray developed by Lister.

Now read the following questions. Then completely fill in the bubble of the correct answer.

1. *Gangrene* is a type of _____ .
   Ⓐ progression
   Ⓑ infection
   Ⓒ bandage

2. What is a synonym for *to get well?*
   Ⓐ microscopic
   Ⓑ progression
   Ⓒ recuperate

3. Which heading is the best for classifying *bandage?*
   Ⓐ Something to Read
   Ⓑ Something to Eat
   Ⓒ Something to Wear

4. *Setback* is an antonym for _____ .
   Ⓐ progression
   Ⓑ infection
   Ⓒ surgeon

5. Unable to see them, doctors before Lister did not realize infections were caused by _____ germs.
   Ⓐ synthetic
   Ⓑ microscopic
   Ⓒ recuperate

6. Which word uses the prefix meaning "very small; minute"?
   Ⓐ infection
   Ⓑ recuperate
   Ⓒ microscopic

# 4 Review Word Meanings

Read the passage below. Then answer the questions about the boldfaced vocabulary words.

## Music and Medicine

Imagine this **scene:** The players take the center of the stage. In the **balcony,** people watch, waiting for the **dramatic** beginning. Instruments sparkle. The **tension** builds as everyone waits for the **orchestra** to begin.

Did you guess that this was an **auditorium** filled with musicians? It is not. There are no **velvet** gowns and satin gloves in this scene, only sterile blue **textiles** made into smocks and latex gloves. It is an operating theater in which the surgeons and nurses are ready to begin an operation. The people watching are medical students. The music is being played to relax the doctors and the patient. Hopefully two **masterpieces** will be experienced here: the music of a symphony and the work of a skilled surgeon.

Now read the following questions. Then completely fill in the bubble of the correct answer.

1. Which set of words below would be in a group with *orchestra?*
   - Ⓐ instruments, hospital gowns, surgeon
   - Ⓑ instruments, marching band, cheerleader
   - Ⓒ instruments, conductor, music

2. Velvet would not be found _____ .
   - Ⓐ on the seats in an auditorium
   - Ⓑ as an instrument in the orchestra
   - Ⓒ in a masterpiece

3. *Championship* is to *sports* as _____ is to *art.*
   - Ⓐ *masterpiece*
   - Ⓑ *velvet*
   - Ⓒ *auditorium*

4. When and where something takes place is the _____ .
   - Ⓐ auditorium
   - Ⓑ balcony
   - Ⓒ scene

5. If you were watching something from above, where would you be sitting?
   - Ⓐ in the auditorium
   - Ⓑ in the balcony
   - Ⓒ with the orchestra

6. Which of the following is an example of a *textile?*
   - Ⓐ cotton
   - Ⓑ plastic
   - Ⓒ slate

**Vocabulary List**

1. **capable**
   (kā′ pə bəl) *adj.*
   being able

2. **instinct**
   (in′ stingkt′) *n.*
   inborn behavior

3. **exposed**
   (ek spōzd′) *v.*
   to be uncovered

4. **rugged**
   (rug′ id) *adj.*
   rough

5. **terrain**
   (tə rān′) *n.*
   region of land

6. **endure**
   (en dŏŏr′) *v.*
   to put up with

7. **provisions**
   (prə vizh′ ənz) *n.*
   supply of food

8. **recover**
   (ri kuv′ ər) *v.*
   to get well again

9. **sacrifice**
   (sak′ rə fīs′) *v.*
   to give up
   something

10. **equipment**
    (i kwip′ mənt) *n.*
    supplies

# "Survival" Vocabulary

**1** **Word Meanings**

## Matching Complete Definitions

 Match each vocabulary word below with its complete definition. Write the letter of the definition in the blank.

1. _____ rugged

2. _____ endure

3. _____ sacrifice

4. _____ instinct

5. _____ exposed

6. _____ equipment

7. _____ provisions

8. _____ capable

9. _____ recover

10. _____ terrain

**a.** an inborn or natural way to act

**b.** stock or supply of food

**c.** having a rough and uneven surface

**d.** having or showing ability

**e.** supplies used or needed for a special purpose

**f.** to get back to normal or healthy condition

**g.** a region or tract of land

**h.** to tolerate or put up with

**i.** to give up for the sake of something else

**j.** to be made known; revealed or uncovered

## Think About It

Each of the Vocabulary List words for this lesson relate to survival. Think about how each word connects to the theme. What other words can you think of in this category?

## 2 Reference Skills

# Finding Parts of Speech

 Complete the Venn diagram below. First look up each vocabulary word in the dictionary to determine its part, or parts, of speech.

**NOUNS**                    **VERBS**

**BOTH**

1. _____

2. _____

3. _____

4. _____

5. _____

6. _____

7. _____

8. _____

• • • • • • • • • • • • • • • • • • • • • • • • • • • • • • • • • • • • • • • •

 Use the words from above to complete the sentences in the passage below.

The hiker did not have an accurate map, so she had to rely on

her natural sense, or _____ to return to the campsite. She was distracted by the rugged

_____ that was causing her to trip and stumble as she walked. A broken toe would take weeks to

_____. Unfortunately her _____ for the week were back with the others, and she was getting hungry. At least she had packed her first-aid kit and other

safety _____. Her heavy backpack was slowing

her down, but she did not want to _____ anything that she might need. Once the trail was

_____ through the overgrown brush, she

was sure she would be able to _____ the long hike back.

## Vocabulary List

1. capable
2. instinct
3. exposed
4. rugged
5. terrain
6. endure
7. provisions
8. recover
9. sacrifice
10. equipment

# 3 Build New Vocabulary

## Root Words

 Read and answer the following question.

1. *Terr* is a Latin root that means "land." Which vocabulary word contains the root *terr* and means "the land of an area"? _____

 Match each word below with its definition.

2. _____ territory

3. _____ terrarium

4. _____ terrace

5. _____ terrestrial

6. _____ terra cotta

**a.** a raised platform of earth, often in a series

**b.** hard, brownish orange earthenware

**c.** a small, enclosed container used to grow plants or house small animals

**d.** living on the land, not in the air, water, or trees

**e.** any large area of land

 Read each sentence below. Complete each sentence with the word from the exercise above that best fits. Write the word in the blank.

7. You can tell that a bird is not a _____ animal because of the time it spends in the air.

8. The _____ in our classroom was set up so that we can study lizards in their environment.

9. The tiles on the floor of our patio were made of

_____.

10. The flat _____ was the result of glaciers smoothing out the land.

Score _____ (Top Score 10)   "Survival" Vocabulary • Build New Vocabulary

 **Word Play**

# Alliteration

 Read each alliterative tongue twister below. Write the vocabulary word that best completes each.

1. Sabrina said she will _____ ice-cream sundaes so that she can slip into her swimsuit this summer.

2. Paloma packed plenty of _____ for Paul's birthday party picnic.

3. Could you call yourself _____ of climbing that incredible cliff?

4. Everyone enjoyed the exciting electronic

   _____ used to examine Earth's exosphere.

5. Tre's trouble with the tumbling

   _____ is the terrible new tenderness in his toes.

6. Evelyn eventually _____ the evidence in exhibit A—the éclair box was empty!

7. Roland raced down the _____ river until his raft ran into a rock and was ruined.

8. The Internet informed me that the intelligent iguana does

   not eat insects by _____.

9. Running in the race through the rain gave Reiko a respiratory rattle. We really hope she will

   _____ rapidly.

10. Elizabeth will _____ a new eating and exercise agenda in order to enter the entertainment industry.

1. **gorge**
(gorj) *n.*
a deep valley

2. **reservoir**
(rez′ ər vwär′) *n.*
place for water
storage

3. **plateau**
(pla tō′) *n.*
flat, raised land

4. **lava**
(lä′ və) *n.*
hot, liquid rock

5. **geologist**
(jē ol′ ə jist) *n.*
scientist who studies
Earth's surface

6. **oasis**
(ō ā′ sis) *n.*
fertile desert area

7. **igneous**
(ig′ nē əs) *adj.*
formed by great heat

8. **mineral**
(min′ ər əl) *n.*
natural substance

9. **sedimentary**
(sed′ ə men′ tə rē)
*adj.* formed by layers

10. **irrigate**
(ir′ i gāt′) *v.*
to supply land with
water

# Earth Words

**1**    **Word Meanings**

## Restatements

 Read each sentence below. Underline the restatements that reflect the meanings of each boldfaced vocabulary word.

1. A **geologist,** or a person who studies the earth, keeps very detailed notes that describe what he or she finds.

2. The hikers took a break to eat their lunch on the **plateau,** the area of flat, raised land, after their difficult climb.

3. The farmer will **irrigate,** or supply water to his land, this year with a long, deep channel that he dug last autumn.

4. Sandstone, limestone, and shale are all examples of **sedimentary** rocks, or rocks that are formed by compressed layers.

5. As we stood at the edge of the cliff, our guide tossed a rock into the **gorge,** the deep valley, that lay before us.

6. You will find the most active volcano in the world at the National Park of Royal Gardens in Hawaii. Hot, liquid rock called **lava** streams from the mouth of the volcano Kilauea.

7. The guide pointed out the **oasis,** the bright, green, fertile area in the desert, when she showed us the video from her trip to Arizona.

8. Our class took a field trip to the **reservoir,** the place for water storage, and learned how they store water for irrigation, conserve wildlife habitats, and provide hydroelectric power.

9. Gold is a **mineral,** a natural substance from the earth.

10. Rocks that are formed by intense heat, **igneous** rocks, were once trapped in small pockets underground and slowly cooled and hardened.

## 2 Reference Skills

# Words with More Than One Meaning

 Read each dictionary entry and the sentences below. Complete each sentence by writing the word that best fits in the blank. Then write the number of the definition you chose in the box.

---

**gorge** (gorj) *n.* **1.** a deep, narrow opening or passage between mountains **2.** a mass that clogs an opening *v.* **3.** to stuff with food

**plateau** (pla tō´) *n.* **1.** an area of flat land raised above the surrounding land **2.** a stage of development

**oasis** (ō ā´ sis) *n.* **1.** a place in a desert that is fertile because it has a supply of water **2.** any place that provides refreshment or relief

**irrigate** (ir´ i gāt) *v.* **1.** to supply with water **2.** to cleanse a wound with a flow of some liquid

---

1. The air-conditioned restaurant was an

_____ to the hot and tired students

after their field trip. ☐

2. Mom told us not to _____ ourselves

when the pizza finally arrived. ☐

3. He suggested that we _____ the lawn
today because we had not had any rain in almost a month.

☐

4. I had reached a _____ where I could
not lose any more weight by doing the same exercises.

☐

5. When we saw the green, lush _____
in the middle of the desert, we thought we were

dreaming. ☐

---

## Vocabulary List

1. *gorge*
2. *reservoir*
3. *plateau*
4. *lava*
5. *geologist*
6. *oasis*
7. *igneous*
8. *mineral*
9. *sedimentary*
10. *irrigate*

## 3 Build New Vocabulary

### Related Word Forms

 Read the words and definitions below. Write the vocabulary word that relates to each word in the blank.

1. *reserve: v.* to set aside; to save until later

   _____

2. *geology: n.* the science of Earth's structure and history

   _____

3. *irrigator: n.* something used to supply land with water

   _____

4. *sediment: n.* rock or earth that settles to the bottom layer

   _____

5. *platform: n.* a raised, flat structure or flooring

   _____

6. *mine: v.* to dig in the earth for coal or other natural

   materials _____

### Think About It

If you call ahead to a restaurant asking them to save a table for your party, you are making *reservations*. What word above relates to *reservations?* How are *reservations* similar to this vocabulary word?

## 4    Word Play

# Where Would You Find It?

 Read each sentence below. Fill in the blank by identifying the vocabulary word that could be found where the answer suggests.

1. Where would you find _____ rock?
Answer: in thin layers of soil and broken rocks near Earth's surface

2. Where would you find _____ rock?
Answer: deep below Earth's surface where hot magma has cooled and hardened

3. Where would you find an _____?
Answer: in an area of Earth that has been dut out

4. Where would you find a _____?
Answer: in an area of Earth that has been dug out (examples are salt, coal, and gold)

5. Where would you find _____?
Answer: erupting from an active volcano or through a crack in Earth's surface

6. Where would you find a person who wants to

_____?
Answer: in a place where the land is dry and has no water

7. Where would you find a _____?
Answer: between steep and rocky mountains

8. Where would you find a _____?
Answer: in a lake used for storing water

9. Where would you find a _____?
Answer: on the plains

10. Where would you find a _____?
Answer: on a site studying Earth and its history

1. **wardrobe**
   (word´ rōb´) *n.*
   collection of clothes

2. **monogram**
   (mon´ ə gram´) *n.*
   design using initials

3. **crinoline**
   (krin´ ə lin) *n.*
   stiff skirt lining

4. **tiara**
   (tē ar´ ə) *n.*
   crown-like piece

5. **corsage**
   (kor säzh´) *n.*
   flower worn by
   women

6. **tuxedo**
   (tuk sē´ dō) *n.*
   formal suit for men

7. **gown**
   (goun) *n.*
   formal dress for
   women

8. **accessories**
   (ak ses´ ə rēs) *n.*
   pieces added

9. **stylish**
   (stī´ lish) *adj.*
   in current fashion

10. **designer**
    (di zī´ nər) *n.*
    person who creates
    styles

# "Fashion" Vocabulary

 **1** **Word Meanings**

## Descriptions

Read each description in the *What It Is* and *What It Is Not* columns. Choose the vocabulary word that best matches the descriptions and write it in the blank.

| What It *Is* | What It *Is Not* | Vocabulary Word |
|---|---|---|
| 1. flowers to wear | flowers for a vase | _____ |
| 2. fashionable | out of date | _____ |
| 3. a fancy dress | denim overalls | _____ |
| 4. a jeweled headpiece | necklace | _____ |
| 5. all of your clothes | comfy, warm robe | _____ |
| 6. creator of new styles | hot, liquid rock | _____ |
| 7. formal suit for men | used for rock climbing | _____ |
| 8. design using initials | one grandparent | _____ |
| 9. added pieces | pants | _____ |
| 10. lining for a full skirt | French pastry | _____ |

• • • • • • • • • • • • • • • • • • • • • • • • • • • • • • • • • • • •

 ## Think About It

For what occasions do women wear corsages, tiaras, or gowns? Where would a man wear a tuxedo? Look through magazines or photo albums to find examples for each vocabulary word.

## 2 Reference Skills

# Using the Internet

*Welcome to the Students'
Super-Duper Search Engine*

Enter your key word search in the box below:

Press enter to see your choices . . .

 Circle the letter of the correct answer for each question below.

1. Which key words would you type to find information on the life and work of designer Gianni Versace?
   a. Gianni Life
   b. Designer Versace
   c. Designer Gianni Versace

2. Which choice from the second screen would give you the best information?
   a. Italian Designers and Their Homes
   b. Gianni Versace–His Life and Work
   c. Versace Perfumes

3. What might you find if you clicked *Versace Perfumes* on the second screen?
   a. information on Versace's life and work
   b. the history of perfume
   c. information on designer perfumes by Versace

4. If the second screen gives you information on Versace's work but not on his life, how might you change your key word search?
   a. Designer Gianni Versace–His Life and Work
   b. Designer Gianni Versooche
   c. Designers

5. If you misspelled a word in your key word search, how would this change your result?
   a. The computer would figure it out.
   b. You might get incorrect information or no information.
   c. The computer will shut down.

## Vocabulary List

1. wardrobe
2. monogram
3. crinoline
4. tiara
5. corsage
6. tuxedo
7. gown
8. accessories
9. stylish
10. designer

# 3 Build New Vocabulary

## Word Parts

 Solve the Word Parts puzzle below.

| Prefix | Meaning | Root | Meaning |
|--------|---------|------|---------|
| 1. *mono-* | one | *gram* | letter |

| Vocabulary Word | Meaning |
|-----------------|---------|
| _____ | _____ |

Match the words below with their definitions. Use a dictionary for help if necessary.

2. _____ monorail      **A.** a letter sent by telegraph

3. _____ monotone      **B.** one syllable

4. _____ telegram      **C.** rules of written language

5. _____ monosyllable  **D.** one rail

6. _____ grammar       **E.** one tone

Use the words from above to complete the sentences below.

7. I sewed a _____ on a blanket for my grandparents using their initials.

8. We parked our car and rode the _____ to town to see the football game.

9. A message sent by electric pulses through a telegraph is called a _____.

10. The guest speaker did not use any expression in his voice; he sounded very _____.

 **Word Play**

# Silly Rhyming Riddles

 Answer each riddle below using a rhyming phrase from the box.

| | | |
|---|---|---|
| corsage garage | drive-in crinoline | stylish starfish |
| designer diner | snap peas | hoedown gown |
| space probe | accessories | |
| wardrobe | tiara era | |

1. What do you call vegetable earrings?

   _____

2. What do you call clothing that is "out of this world"?

   _____

3. Where would you park your flowers?

   _____

4. Where do trendsetters order hot dogs and milkshakes?

   _____

5. What do you call a very fashionable echinoderm?

   _____

6. What fancy dress do you wear to square dance?

   _____

7. What do you call a skirt lining worn to the movies?

   _____

8. What do you call a period of time when headpieces were

   worn? _____

**Vocabulary List**

1. **pinpoint**
   (pin´ point´) *v.*
   to locate exactly

2. **underhanded**
   (un´ dər han´ did)
   *adv.* sneaky

3. **high-strung**
   (hī´ strung´) *adj.*
   very tense

4. **overpass**
   (ō´ vər pas´) *n.*
   bridge over a road

5. **widespread**
   (wīd´ spred) *adj.*
   extending over a
   large area

6. **wrongdoing**
   (wrong´ doo ing) *n.*
   bad behavior

7. **overhaul**
   (ō´ vər hôl´) *v.*
   to fully repair

8. **daydream**
   (dā´ drēm´) *n.*
   a dreamy imagining

9. **deadline**
   (ded´ līn´) *n.*
   time set for
   completion

10. **streamlined**
    (strēm´ līnd´) *adj.*
    smooth in design

# Compound Words

## 1 Word Meanings

## Meanings of Compound Words

 Read the definitions below. Write the vocabulary word that best matches each definition.

1. the exact location or identity

   _____

2. the act of doing something that is not right

   _____

3. to look at carefully and make needed repairs

   _____

4. extending over a large area

   _____

5. a set time by which something must be completed

   _____

6. very tense or nervous; excitable

   _____

7. a dreamy imagining done while awake

   _____

8. a bridge or road that crosses over another bridge or road

   _____

9. done in secret; in a sly way

   _____

10. designed to be smooth and have little resistance

    _____

## 2 Reference Skills

# Using Compound Words

Match the parts given in the exercise below with the vocabulary word parts in the box to make compound words. Write each compound word in the blank.
(**Hint**: One word part from the box is used twice.)

| | | | | |
|---|---|---|---|---|
| wrong | spread | point | over | handed |
| stream | over | strung | day | line |

1. _____ dream

2. dead _____

3. high- _____

4. _____ haul

5. _____ pass

6. pin _____

7. _____ lined

8. under _____

9. wide _____

10. _____ doing

• • • • • • • • • • • • • • • • • • • • • • • • • • • • • • • • • • • •

Now complete the sentences below using five of the compound words you made above.

11. Amber, who was already a very _____ student, was losing sleep over the upcoming test.

12. It did not take long for the chicken pox to become _____ in our school.

13. The _____ speedboat slipped easily through the rough water.

14. Juwan stayed up all night to complete his science fair project before tomorrow's _____.

15. Jake did poorly on his exam due to the fact that he would rather _____ than study.

## Vocabulary List

1. *pinpoint*
2. *underhanded*
3. *high-strung*
4. *overpass*
5. *widespread*
6. *wrongdoing*
7. *overhaul*
8. *daydream*
9. *deadline*
10. *streamlined*

# 3 Build New Vocabulary

## Context Clues

 Use the words in the box to make compound words and complete the sentences in the passage below.

| bold | day | home | class | after | line |
|------|-----|------|-------|-------|------|
| book | under | note | light | text | point |

### How to Study

It is important to develop your own set of study skills. The skills that work for one person in your

_____room might not work for you. However, good study skills almost always involve some of the following basic practices.

First, set up an area at home that is well-lit, quiet, and free from distractions. Set aside a specific amount of time

in the _____noon for doing your

_____work. Try reading the pages assigned in

your text_____ out loud. It sometimes helps to hear your own voice reading new information.

You might also try writing down important points in your

_____book. You are more likely to remember information if you read and write it. Taking good notes helps

you pin_____ information more easily.

Many _____books will

high_____ important terms by

_____facing or _____lining

them. You can create an out_____ to organize your written information and help you remember how it fits together. Be careful not to spend your study time lost in a

_____dream. Concentrate on your work and always do your best.

Score _____ (Top Score 12)   Compound Words • Build New Vocabulary

 **Word Play**

## Double Take

 Choose a word from the box that matches both definitions for each item. Write the word on the spaces.

| gorge | accessories | ivory | pinpoint | underhanded |
|---|---|---|---|---|
| close | recover | crooked | condition | cabinet |

**Definition One** **Definition Two**

1. a very small amount — to locate precisely

2. to eat too much — land between two mountains

3. to get well again — to put on a new covering

4. elephant tusks — a creamy, white color

5. to treat one's hair — one's state of being

6. the president's helpers — a place to store things

7. bent — dishonest

8. pieces added for looks — people who help with a crime

9. near — to shut

10. a way to throw a ball — a shady dealing

 Now earn two extra points by unscrambling the circled letters from above to make two new words below.

**Vocabulary List**

1. **ghetto**
   (get′ ō) *n.*
   separated area
   of town

2. **heritage**
   (her′ i tij) *n.*
   something handed
   down

3. **ambassador**
   (am bas′ ə dər) *n.*
   a representative

4. **bond**
   (bond) *n.*
   a uniting tie

5. **bazaar**
   (bə zär′) *n.*
   a marketplace

6. **pueblo**
   (pwe′ blō) *n.*
   a Native American
   village

7. **bongos**
   (bong′ gōs) *n.*
   small drums

8. **origin**
   (or′ i jin) *n.*
   starting point

9. **civilization**
   (siv′ ə lə zā′ shən) *n.*
   way of life

10. **community**
    (kə mo͞o′ ni tē) *n.*
    where people live

# Vocabulary for Culture

## ① Word Meanings

### Synonyms

 Read the sentences below. Circle the synonym of the underlined word in each sentence.

1. People who live together form a <u>neighborhood</u> whether they are living in Native American pueblos or urban apartment buildings.

   bazaar          origin          community

2. A person who speaks for his or her country in another country is an elected <u>representative</u>.

   pueblo          ambassador          civilization

3. Music is a tie that can <u>unite</u> many cultures. Afro-Latin music combines the bongos with other traditional jazz instruments.

   bazaar          heritage          bond

4. <u>Drums</u> are instruments you beat with your hands.

   humanity          ghetto          bongos

5. An outdoor shopping area is called a <u>market</u>.

   bazaar          ambassador          bongos

6. Our <u>inheritance</u> includes the traditions and customs handed down to us by our ancestors.

   heritage          courtesy          pueblo

7. The way of life of a group of people is their <u>culture</u>.

   community          civilization          bazaar

8. An etymologist is a person who studies the history of words, from their <u>beginning</u> to their present form.

   origin          bazaar          bond

## ② Reference Skills

# Dictionary Sentences

Write the letter of the sentence that uses the given vocabulary word correctly.

1. _____ civilization
   a. Many modern tools stem back to the civilization of the ancient Greek people.
   b. We studied the civilization of early computers.

2. _____ ambassador
   a. Carlos Pascual is the U.S. ambassador to Ukraine.
   b. I have to organize my ambassador before school starts.

3. _____ bazaar
   a. My aunt bought fresh fruit, a necklace, and a book of poetry at the bazaar last Saturday.
   b. This purple bazaar fell right out of that tree.

4. _____ origin
   a. The painting was an origin; it was the only one of its kind.
   b. They discovered the fire's origin in the basement.

5. _____ heritage
   a. We could see in her family picture that curly, red hair is clearly a part of Claire's heritage.
   b. The heritage of the chalkboard was falling apart.

6. _____ bond
   a. The bond of friendship was strong between Thomas Jefferson and John Adams.
   b. My friend's bond only plays hits from the 1980's.

7. _____ ghetto
   a. He arrived at the party looking ghetto.
   b. The Jewish ghettos in Poland were to be surrounded by barbed wire and brick walls.

8. _____ bongos
   a. The bongos were played in the background to add rhythm and mood.
   b. She said she was going bongos from all of the noise.

## Vocabulary List

1. ghetto
2. heritage
3. ambassador
4. bond
5. bazaar
6. pueblo
7. bongos
8. origin
9. civilization
10. community

# 3 Build New Vocabulary

## Related Words

 Match the words below with their definitions.

1. _____ commune

2. _____ civilized

3. _____ original

4. _____ hereditary

**A.** like no other

**B.** able to be passed on from an ancestor

**C.** when people talk or gather together

**D.** educated in the art, sciences, and government

 Use the words from above to complete the passage below.

### The Jewish Ghettos

When Germany invaded Poland and the Soviet Union before World War II, more than two million Jews were under German control. Many of these

Jewish people were moved from their own _____ world to a dirty, run-down, sectioned-off part of town known as the ghettos.

A single apartment in the Jewish Ghetto usually had several families living in it. Disease, hunger, and cold temperatures forced many Jews to gather

together and _____ with one another about the importance of survival. Young people living in the ghettos tried to continue their education by going to secret classes set up by Jewish adults. Jewish children made

_____ toys out of bits of cloth and wood that they found. The Jewish people struggled through many hard times, but their

_____ strength passed down by their ancestors proved that they were a strong people whose freedom could not be confined, even in the guarded ghettos.

# 4 Word Play

## Help! There's an *Ant*onym in My Word!

 Look at the following coded vocabulary words. Replace the underlined word part in each with its antonym from the box. (**Hint:** The antonyms will not always give you the correct spelling of the actual vocabulary words, so be certain to check each word carefully.)

| Antonyms | | | | | | | |
|---|---|---|---|---|---|---|---|
| blow | go | bass | civil | come | age | on | or |

| Coded Vocabulary Words | Actual Vocabulary Words |
|---|---|
| 1. pue<u>inhale</u> | pue_____ |
| 2. <u>wild</u>ization | _____ization |
| 3. b<u>off</u>d | b_____d |
| 4. am<u>soprano</u>ador | am_____ador |
| 5. herit<u>youth</u> | herit_____ |
| 6. bon<u>stop</u>s | bon_____s |
| 7. <u>leave</u>munity | _____munity |
| 8. <u>and</u>igin | _____igin |

. . . . . . . . . . . . . . . . . . . . . . . . . . . . . . . . . . . . . . . .

 ## Think About It

Using words in unusual ways is a great way to create special written and spoken codes for communicating. Think about the many ways you can change words to make a secret language and why you would want to.

# Vocabulary Review

### ① Review Word Meanings

Read the passage below. Then answer the questions about the boldfaced vocabulary words.

## All About Spiders

The itsy, bitsy spider deserves our respect. Spiders are amazing. Different spiders are able to **endure** extremes, such as the cold of the tundra and the heat of the desert. Against odds, spiders not only survive, but do so extremely well. About 36,000 different kinds of spiders live together much like a **civilization** of people. Some are smaller than a dot. Others are as big as a dinner plate. While most spiders prefer to live alone, some live in **communities.**

**Geologists** sometimes accidentally discover spiders when they are poking around under rocks and in crevices. Without saying that spiders are nervous, you might say spiders are **"high-strung."** They are **capable** of using their silk to "balloon," or float, from place to place. They use their silk for other things, too, such as protecting their eggs and catching their prey. How do they learn to do this? They don't! It's **instinct!**

Now read the following questions. Then completely fill in the bubble of the correct answer.

1. Which word below is related to *geology?*
   - Ⓐ capable
   - Ⓑ geologists
   - Ⓒ civilization

2. Which word below is a synonym for *nervous?*
   - Ⓐ high-strung
   - Ⓑ civilizations
   - Ⓒ communities

3. To have the ability to do something is to be _____.
   - Ⓐ civilized
   - Ⓑ high-strung
   - Ⓒ capable

4. What could you call a group of people who live in a neighborhood?
   - Ⓐ endure
   - Ⓑ community
   - Ⓒ instinct

5. Which example below is not an example of *endure?*
   - Ⓐ studying long and hard for a test
   - Ⓑ rebuilding the blocks your brother keeps knocking down
   - Ⓒ taking your ball and going home

6. Which statement is true based on the passage above?
   - Ⓐ Spiders use their silk to protect their eggs.
   - Ⓑ Geologists never discover spiders while studying the earth.
   - Ⓒ Spiders teach their young how to spin webs.

# ② Review Word Meanings

Read the passage below. Then answer the questions about the boldfaced vocabulary words.

## Be Aware! Spiders are Everywhere!

Spiders are so **widespread** they can be found anywhere on Earth—from deep, cool **gorges** to high, sunny **plateaus.** Some have even gone to outer space. Whether you visit the **lava** flows in Hawaii, the **rugged terrain** of Mount Everest, or the frozen arctic, you can find spiders for travel companions.

You may find fisher spiders that actually walk on water in a **reservoir.** Crab spiders hide in flowers of all kinds, maybe even in that beautiful **corsage** you are wearing! You may even discover them in your **provisions** when you go camping! Yuck! Look under **overpasses** and under tables at **bazaars.** Be aware that spiders will begin a **migration** from the outdoors to the cozy indoors as cold weather approaches. But don't worry. If you don't bother them, they won't bother you.

Now read the following questions. Then completely fill in the bubble of the correct answer.

1. Which of the following words is a related form of *migration?*
   Ⓐ migraine
   Ⓑ migrate
   Ⓒ mirage

2. Which of the following multiple meanings for *rugged* is used in the passage above?
   Ⓐ able to endure physical hardship
   Ⓑ difficult to do
   Ⓒ rough and uneven; jagged surface

3. Which of the phrases below defines *rugged?*
   Ⓐ a rough, rocky trail
   Ⓑ a cool, grassy trail
   Ⓒ a smooth, icy trail

4. A reservoir in a car holds liquid for washing the windshield. What else does *reservoir* mean?
   Ⓐ a loud, harsh thunderstorm
   Ⓑ a pond or lake used for storing water
   Ⓒ washing off with water

5. Which of the following pairs are both compound words?
   Ⓐ plateau, corsage
   Ⓑ widespread, overpass
   Ⓒ bazaar, widespread

6. Which sentence uses *gorges* correctly?
   Ⓐ That gown is absolutely gorges.
   Ⓑ The gorges were lined with vines, jagged rocks, and waterfalls.
   Ⓒ I gave her four gorges for her birthday.

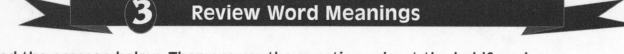

Read the passage below. Then answer the questions about the boldfaced vocabulary words.

# How Do Spiders Survive?

Spiders face many challenges, but they have instincts to help them survive. Birds, lizards, snakes, toads, wasps, and even other spiders eat spiders. How do spiders fight back? They use many tricks. It would be impossible to **pinpoint** one skill as the most important. While some spiders are poisonous and bite, they cannot be accused of any **wrongdoings.** They are just protecting themselves.

Female spiders protect their young by **sacrificing** their own time and energy. Some female spiders carry egg sacs around with them until their spiderlings, or baby spiders, hatch. Some carry the spiderlings on their backs. Others, such as Desert spiders, dig holes in the sand to bury their egg sacs where the temperature is cooler because the spiderlings cannot be **exposed** to the hot sun.

Unfortunately, humans are the biggest threat to spiders. Chemicals used to kill pests, as well a changing environment due to population growth, threaten many spiders. Sadly, spiders that cannot **recover** from these changes in their environments will become extinct.

. . . . . . . . . . . . . . . . . . . . . . . . . . . . . . . . . . . . . . . . . . . . . . . . . . . . . . . . . . . . . . . . . . . . . . .

Now read the following questions. Then completely fill in the bubble of the correct answer.

1. When female spiders pay more attention to helping their spiderlings than to taking care of themselves, they are making _____ .
   Ⓐ sacrifices
   Ⓑ instincts
   Ⓒ wrongdoings

2. Which definition below matches the way *recover* is used in the passage above?
   Ⓐ to put a new cover on
   Ⓑ to cover again
   Ⓒ to get back to a normal condition

3. Which of the following words is related to *expose?*
   Ⓐ exposure
   Ⓑ expensive
   Ⓒ exactly

4. Which definition below matches the way *pinpoint* is used in the passage above?
   Ⓐ the point of a pin
   Ⓑ to locate precisely
   Ⓒ a narrow area

5. Which of the following would not be an *instinct?*
   Ⓐ spinning a sticky web
   Ⓑ hatching out of an egg
   Ⓒ reading a newspaper

# ④ Review Word Meanings

Read the passage below. Then answer the questions about the boldfaced vocabulary words.

## Spider Friends

Not everyone dislikes spiders. Some people actually honor spiders and treat them with **courtesy.** Spiders have been used as characters in stories and in artwork. The story of Grandmother Spider is part of the **heritage** of Native Americans who live in **pueblos.** The story explains the **origin** of Earth. Rice farmers in China protect spiders and use them to control crop-eating pests. And, of course, you know of the superhero character that was based on a spider. Some children probably have a whole **wardrobe** of spider clothing from this character alone.

How about you? Are you ready to help **overhaul** the image of spiders? Perhaps if you watched and learned more about spiders you could be an **ambassador** for them. With very little **equipment**—just a jar and a magnifying glass—you could observe and study the helpful and amazing ways of spiders. Who knows? Maybe you will become known as Super Spider Saver. You could have a triple *S* **monogram** on all your clothes. Children everywhere would **daydream** about you and your amazing spider rescues.

Now read the following questions. Then completely fill in the bubble of the correct answer.

1. Which of the following is the best definition for *overhaul* as it is used in the passage above?
   Ⓐ to haul over
   Ⓑ to carry from place to place
   Ⓒ to repair

2. In which sentence below does the context clue help you understand the correct meaning of *ambassador?*
   Ⓐ You can be an ambassador, or spokesperson, for better treatment of spiders.
   Ⓑ You can be an ambassador, or enemy, for better treatment of spiders.
   Ⓒ You can be an ambassador, or monogram, for better treatment of spiders.

3. Which statement is *not* true according to the passage above?
   Ⓐ The story of Grandmother Spider explains the beginning of Earth.
   Ⓑ You can study spiders with just a jar and a magnifying glass.
   Ⓒ Rice farmers in China kill spiders to protect their crops.

4. Which of the following is the best definition for *pueblos* as it is used in the passage above?
   Ⓐ villages
   Ⓑ Native American people
   Ⓒ adobe

5. Which of the following words is a synonym for *origin?*
   Ⓐ problem
   Ⓑ solution
   Ⓒ beginning

1. **correspond**
(kor´ ə spond´) v.
to communicate by writing letters

2. **inform**
(in form´) v.
to give information

3. **slang**
(slang) n.
informal speech

4. **interrupt**
(in´ tə rupt´) v.
to cause a break in speech

5. **reply**
(ri plī´) v.
to answer or respond

6. **request**
(ri kwest´) v.
to ask for

7. **transmit**
(trans mit´) v.
to send out signals

8. **recommend**
(rek´ ə mend´) v.
to speak well of

9. **intercept**
(in´ tər sept´) v.
to stop on the way

10. **remote**
(ri mōt´) adj.
not near

# "Communication" Vocabulary

## 1 Word Meanings

### Sentence Completion

 Read the sentences below. Choose the vocabulary word that completes each sentence and write it in the blank.

1. We were waiting to hear our teacher _____ after asking him for extra recess time.

2. Tia and her pen pal _____ with each other every month.

3. I _____ that you try the fresh garden salad with your dinner.

4. Because they were living in such a _____ area of town, Brit and Bonnie were on the school bus for an hour each morning.

5. I _____ only that you do your best.

6. Before you _____ me, I want to tell you the entire story.

7. We laughed when we heard our parents and their friends using the _____ that was popular when they were kids.

8. Our teacher will _____ this note if she sees me pass it to you.

9. The front page of our Web site will _____ people of our school's outdoor festival.

10. If you want to walk, dance, skip, or jump, your brain will _____ signals to your body telling it to move accordingly.

## ② Reference Skills

## Using a Thesaurus

 Read each thesaurus entry below. Then answer the questions.

---

**inform** *v.* to tell, make known, advise, acquaint, fill in
*ant.* conceal, hide, learn

**reply** *v.* to answer, retort, respond, quip, echo
*ant.* ask, demand, question, request

**request** *v.* to ask, solicit, implore, beg

---

1. What part of speech is given for *inform, reply,* and *request?* _____

2. For which words are antonyms given?

   _____

3. Which antonyms are given for the word that means "to advise"? _____

4. Circle the following words that are synonyms for *request.*

   ask        solicit        implore        promise        beg

• • • • • • • • • • • • • • • • • • • • • • • • • • • • • • • • • •

Read the vocabulary words below. Using a thesaurus as a reference, circle the synonyms and draw a box around the antonyms. (**Hint:** Not all the words are used as synonyms or antonyms.)

5. *intercept:* block, transmit, stop, enjoy, allow

6. *remote:* close, near, far, distant, control

7. *correspond:* write letters, communicate, need, disagree

8. *interrupt:* continue, stop, disturb, wish, halt

---

## Vocabulary List

1. correspond

2. inform

3. slang

4. interrupt

5. reply

6. request

7. transmit

8. recommend

9. intercept

10. remote

# 3 Build New Vocabulary

## Suffixes *-er* and *-or*

The suffixes *-er* and *-or* can be added to verbs to form nouns. Add the suffixes *-er* and *-or* to the words below. Then finish writing the definition of each word. (**Hint:** You might want to check your spellings in a dictionary.)

1. broadcast + er = _____

someone who _____

2. inform + er = _____

someone who _____

3. request + er = _____

someone who _____

4. intercept + or = _____

someone who _____

5. transmit + er = _____

someone who _____

6. challenge + er = _____

someone who _____

7. develop + er = _____

someone who _____

8. employ + er = _____

someone who _____

9. promote + er = _____

someone who _____

10. edit + or = _____

someone who _____

Score _____ (Top Score 20) "Communication" Vocabulary • Build New Vocabulary

## 4 Word Play

# The 411 on Slang

 Match each slang expression with its definition below. Write the letter of the correct definition in the blank.

**Slang Terms**

1. _____ kid

2. _____ beat

3. _____ far out

4. _____ right on

5. _____ shady

6. _____ on the back burner

7. _____ twenty-four seven

8. _____ chicken

9. _____ dish out

10. _____ good to go

11. _____ groove

12. _____ keep it real

13. _____ hobnob

14. _____ peeps

15. _____ go bananas

**Definitions**

**A.** *adj.* tired

**B.** *adj.* not the most important thing

**C.** *adj.* ready; on schedule

**D.** *n.* one who is afraid

**E.** *v.* to go crazy

**F.** *v.* to stay true to yourself; to not be fake

**G.** *n.* people

**H.** *n.* a young person

**I.** *v.* to give

**J.** *adj.* unclear, misleading, or illegal

**K.** *adj.* phrase of approval; it is okay

**L.** *adj.* excellent

**M.** *v.* to dance

**N.** *adj.* all the time

**O.** *v.* to spend time with the the upper class

1. **minimum**
(min′ ə məm) *n.*
the least amount

2. **dissect**
(di sekt′) *v.*
to cut apart

3. **project**
(prə jekt′) *v.*
to throw forward

4. **minus**
(mī′ nəs) *prep.*
reduced by; less

5. **inject**
(in jekt′) *v.*
to put in

6. **vacant**
(vā′ kənt) *adj.*
unoccupied or empty

7. **section**
(sek′ shən) *n.*
a part cut off from
the rest

8. **minor**
(mī′ nər) *adj.*
lesser in size or
degree

9. **evacuate**
(i vak′ ū āt′) *v.*
to leave or empty out

10. **intersect**
(in′ tər sekt′) *v.*
to cut across

# Words from Latin

**1** **Word Meanings**

## Analogies

 Complete each analogy below using a vocabulary word.

1. *right* is to *correct* as

   *empty* is to _____

2. *bell* is to *ring* as

   *voice* is to _____

3. *hand* is to *write* as

   *needle* is to _____

4. *song* is to *tune* as

   *crisscross* is to _____

5. *sweet* is to *sour* as

   _____ is to *major*

6. *large* is to *small* as

   *maximum* is to _____

7. *add* is to *plus* as

   *subtract* is to _____

8. *student* is to *classroom* as

   _____ is to *whole*

9. *find* is to *discover* as

   *leave* is to _____

10. *mend* is to *repair* as

    _____ is to *cut*

## 2 Reference Skills

# Phonetic Spellings

Read the sentences below. Circle the phonetic spellings that show how the underlined words would be pronounced, according to how the words are used. Use a dictionary for help if necessary.

1. A science fair <u>project</u> takes a lot of planning and research.
proj´ ekt        prə jekt´

2. On stage you must <u>project</u> your voice so the audience can hear you.
proj´ ekt        prə jekt´

3. That strange-looking <u>object</u> is an early version of the telephone.
ob´ jikt        əb jekt´

4. The angry lawyer jumped up and shouted, "I <u>object</u>!"
ob´ jikt        əb jekt´

5. A kangaroo rat is at home in the <u>desert</u>.
dez´ ərt        di zûrt´

6. The captain of a sinking ship would never <u>desert</u> the passengers.
dez´ ərt        di zûrt´

7. A sloth is <u>content</u> to spend many hours not moving at all.
kon´ tent        kən tent´

8. What is the water <u>content</u> in the human body?
kon´ tent        kən tent´

9. Be certain not to get <u>close</u> to the fire!
klōs        klōz

10. <u>Close</u> your book and get out a pencil.
klōs        klōz

11. The <u>dove</u> was able to fly away from the cat.
duv        dōv

12. The otter <u>dove</u> into the water looking for a shellfish.
duv        dōv

## Vocabulary List

1. minimum
2. dissect
3. project
4. minus
5. inject
6. vacant
7. section
8. minor
9. evacuate
10. intersect

# 3 Build New Vocabulary

## Latin Roots

Read each Latin root and its meaning below. Then choose the vocabulary words that include the root mentioned to complete the sentences in each passage. Write the words in the blanks.

---

*min:* small or less

Patrick is very excited about playing _____

league baseball someday. He takes the _____

age for drafted players, 18, _____ his own age to see how long he will have to wait for his first chance to try out for the team.

---

*sect:* cut

The first step in our printmaking art project was to cut

apart, or _____, a wooden log. This

_____ of wood was taken from the original log and placed faceup for sanding. When it was smooth, we applied blue paint on one half and yellow paint on the

other. Where the colors _____ in the middle, it looks green.

---

*ject:* throw

The relay race required one person to _____ water into the balloons, tie them, and carefully hand them to

his or her partner. The partner had to _____ the balloon toward the bull's-eye to try to knock the teacher into the tub of water.

# 4 Word Play

## Get a Clue

 Write each hidden vocabulary word in the blank. (**Hint:** Think about the meaning of the sentences, and look at the underlined letters.)

1. My Uncle <u>Se</u>rgio began the <u>c</u>ele<u>brat</u>ion by cutting the cake.

   _____

2. She put the love letter <u>in</u> the pocket of her three-sub<u>ject</u>

   notebook. _____

3. <u>Mini</u> was surprised when she counted the <u>mums</u> in her garden to see that there were fewer than ever before.

   _____

4. The <u>pr</u>oblem with the CD player is that it e<u>ject</u>s in the

   middle of every song. _____

5. I am looking inside the <u>v</u>ault but <u>cannot</u> see anything. I

   guess it is empty. _____

6. Mr. <u>Minn</u>ow is the sh<u>ortest</u> teacher in our school.

   _____

7. The teacher <u>di</u>vided the <u>squash seed</u> down the middle for

   our science pro<u>ject</u>. _____

8. W<u>inter</u> Street cuts across the new <u>section</u> of town.

   _____

9. <u>Miss</u> Nelson ru<u>ns</u> five miles every morning beca<u>use</u> she is

   trying to lose weight. _____

10. After finding the refrigerator empty, we asked <u>Eva</u>, "Where are all the <u>cu</u>cumbers?" She replied, "I <u>ate</u> them."

   _____

**Vocabulary List**

1. **shame**
   (shām) *n.*
   embarrassment from
   wrongdoings

2. **tranquil**
   (trang′ kwəl) *adj.*
   peaceful

3. **wistful**
   (wist′ fəl) *adj.*
   sadly wishing

4. **jealous**
   (jel′ əs) *adj.*
   wanting what
   others have

5. **indifferent**
   (in dif′ ər ənt) *adj.*
   uncaring

6. **despise**
   (di spīz′) *v.*
   to hate

7. **ecstatic**
   (ek stat′ ik) *adj.*
   overwhelmed
   with joy

8. **nauseated**
   (nô′ zē āt′ id) *adj.*
   sickened

9. **edgy**
   (ej′ ē) *adj.*
   impatient; nervous

10. **appalled**
    (ə pôld′) *adj.*
    filled with horror
    or shock

# Vocabulary for Feelings

 **1** Word Meanings

## Identifying

 Use the underlined clues to help you choose the vocabulary word that best fits.

1. Jaime <u>wishes he had</u> his neighbor's new video game.

   Jaime feels _____.

2. Elaine is <u>extremely happy</u> about winning these tickets.

   Elaine feels _____.

3. April was <u>shocked and horrified</u> by her brother's bad behavior.

   April felt _____.

4. Wendell is <u>sadly wishing</u> he could join his friends.

   Wendell feels _____.

5. DeAndre <u>strongly hates</u> asparagus and refuses to eat it.

   DeAndre _____s asparagus.

6. Salali feels <u>embarrassed</u> about telling her mother a lie.

   Salali feels _____.

7. Terrance sat relaxing <u>peacefully</u> on the back porch.

   Terrance felt _____.

8. Emanuel paced around the room <u>impatiently</u>.

   Emanuel felt _____.

9. Ian <u>didn't care</u> about the change of plans.

   Ian felt _____.

10. Natalie was <u>sickened</u> by the smell in the laboratory.

    Natalie felt _____.

# Reference Skills
## Word Maps

 Look at each word map below carefully. Use a dictionary and a thesaurus to fill in the empty boxes.

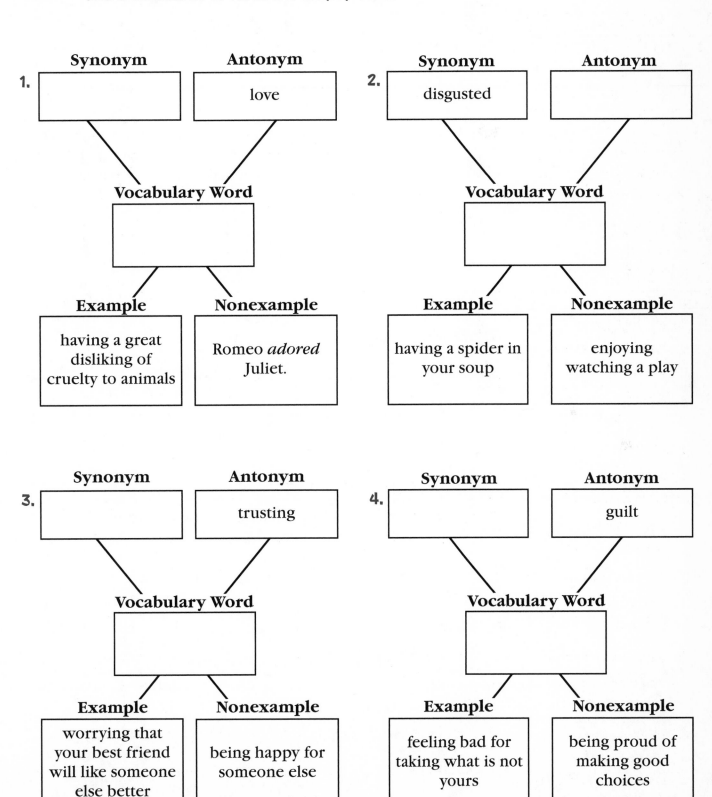

**1.**

**Synonym**

**Antonym**
love

**Vocabulary Word**

**Example**
having a great disliking of cruelty to animals

**Nonexample**
Romeo *adored* Juliet.

**2.**

**Synonym**
disgusted

**Antonym**

**Vocabulary Word**

**Example**
having a spider in your soup

**Nonexample**
enjoying watching a play

**3.**

**Synonym**

**Antonym**
trusting

**Vocabulary Word**

**Example**
worrying that your best friend will like someone else better

**Nonexample**
being happy for someone else

**4.**

**Synonym**

**Antonym**
guilt

**Vocabulary Word**

**Example**
feeling bad for taking what is not yours

**Nonexample**
being proud of making good choices

## Vocabulary List

1. shame
2. tranquil
3. wistful
4. jealous
5. indifferent
6. despise
7. ecstatic
8. nauseated
9. edgy
10. appalled

# 3 Build New Vocabulary

## The Suffix -ful

Answer the question below.

1. The suffix -ful means "full of." This suffix is added to nouns to form adjectives. Which vocabulary word has

the suffix -ful? _____

Add the suffix -ful to each word below. Then write the meanings of the new adjectives you formed. Use a dictionary to check your spelling.

| Adjective | Meaning |
|---|---|
| 2. shame _____ | full of _____ |
| 3. beauty _____ | full of _____ |
| 4. play _____ | full of _____ |
| 5. care _____ | full of _____ |
| 6. fright _____ | full of _____ |
| 7. peace _____ | full of _____ |

Complete each sentence below using the new adjectives you formed above.

8. A rain forest is an incredibly _____ place with lush plants and exotic wildlife.

9. We must be _____ to preserve the rain forests and their inhabitants.

10. It would be _____ to endanger the way of life in the rain forest.

Score _____ (Top Score 16)   Vocabulary for Feelings • Build New Vocabulary

## 4   Word Play

# Spoonerisms

 Read the spoonerisms below. Rewrite the boldfaced words so each sentence is correct. Then underline the vocabulary words in your answers.

**1.** I was **jo sealous** when I saw his new bike.

_____

**2.** My mom told us that she **wespises** pulling **deeds** out of

the garden. _____

**3.** Later he felt **tame** for **shaking** the money that he found.

_____

**4.** The puppies **wooked listfully** out from their cages at the

pet store. _____

**5.** Quiet music and a cool **treeze** created a **branquil** mood

on the patio. _____

**6.** My grandma was **mepalled** by the **apess** in my bedroom.

_____

**7.** When we suggested a vacation, she was **somedifferent**
about going **inplace** new.

_____

**8.** When he saw the A+ on his **ecstabulary** test, he was

**vocatic.** _____

**9.** She was **eeling fedgy** before auditioning for the school

play. _____

**10.** The rocky boat ride left the **nausengers passeated**

for hours. _____

1. **dispute**
(di spūt´) v.
to argue

2. **persuade**
(pər swād´) v.
to win over

3. **confront**
(kən frunt´) v.
to face with

4. **passive**
(pās´ iv) adj.
not active

5. **opinion**
(ə pin´ yən) n.
what one thinks

6. **irk**
(ûrk) v.
to annoy

7. **strategy**
(strat´ i jē) n.
a plan

8. **offensive**
(ə fen´ siv) adj.
rude or unpleasant

9. **resolution**
(rez´ ə lōō´ shən) n.
a solution

10. **conviction**
(kən vik´ shən) n.
a strong belief

# Vocabulary for Debate

## (1) Word Meanings

### Antonyms

 Write the vocabulary word that is an antonym of the boldfaced word or words in each sentence below.

1. Queen Hatshepsut had to **discourage** the Egyptians from accepting her as their ruler. _____

2. Men in the court came up with a **spontaneous act** to accuse Queen Hatshepsut of being dishonest.

   _____

3. However, it was Queen Hatshepsut's **weak belief** that she was meant to rule. _____

4. In Lord Rensomb's opinion, it was **pleasant** that a woman would be "king." _____

5. Lord Rensomb's sour attitude would **delight** Queen Hatshepsut. _____

6. The Queen would **hide from** those who thought she was too weak to rule. _____

7. Instead of being passive, the "king" settled each **agreement** among her officials. _____

8. Queen Hatshepsut worked to find an **argument** to solve any problems in the court. _____

• • • • • • • • • • • • • • • • • • • • • • • • • • • • • • • • • •

### 💡 Think About It

The Egyptian princess, Hatshepsut, was fourteen when she married a king. After the king died, she ruled Upper and Lower Egypt for more than twenty years. Check out *His Majesty, Queen Hatshepsut,* by Dorothy Sharp Carter, to learn more about Hatshepsut.

## ② Reference Skills

# Multiple Meanings

Read each dictionary entry and the example sentences below. Write the word that best completes each sentence in the blank. Then write the number of the definition you used in the box.

---

**conviction** *n.* **1.** the state of being found or proved guilty of a crime in a court or by law: *The criminal has three convictions on her record.* **2.** a strong belief or opinion: *Lawyers must argue their cases with conviction.*

**dispute** *v.* **1.** to debate or quarrel about; discuss; argue: *Whether or not to buy a new car was the issue disputed at our last family meeting.* **2.** to deny or question the validity, accuracy, or existence of; express doubt or opposition to: *His guilt cannot be disputed; it is certain that he committed the crime.*

**offensive** *adj.* **1.** causing resentment, anger, or displeasure; giving offense: *Eloise's neighbors found her behavior offensive.* **2.** unpleasant to the senses; disagreeable: *The smell of grilled hamburgers can be offensive to vegetarians.* **3.** relating to or used for attack: *A sword is an offensive weapon.*

---

1. ☐ Anne Frank's diary entries prove her

   _____ that every person's life is important.

2. ☐ Do you _____ the existence of life on other planets?

3. ☐ The debate teams _____ ten different topics in one hour.

4. ☐ Only 20 minutes after hearing the closing arguments,

   the jury returned with a _____.

5. ☐ All armies need _____ and defensive strategies in wartime.

6. ☐ The Queen considers it to be _____ if you do not bow when you meet her.

---

## Vocabulary List

1. dispute
2. persuade
3. confront
4. passive
5. opinion
6. irk
7. strategy
8. offensive
9. resolution
10. conviction

# 3 Build New Vocabulary

## Adjective Forms

 Combine each vocabulary word and suffix below to form an adjective. Write the adjective in the blank. Use a dictionary to check your spelling.

1. irk + *-some* = _____

2. persuade + *-ive* = _____

3. strategy + *-ic* = _____

4. dispute + *-able* = _____

 Read the sentences below. Choose the adjective that you formed above that best completes each sentence, and write it in the blank.

5. Today the fact that the world is round is not

_____.

6. People often carry _____ posters in Washington, D. C., to convince lawmakers to listen to their opinions.

7. Do you think that painting the ceiling of the Sistine Chapel while he was lying on his back was an

_____ job for Michelangelo?

8. If a television ad makes you want to buy a product, it is

_____.

9. The sound of a baby crying loudly when you are trying to

sleep can be _____.

10. The football team's _____ decision to kick instead of run worked, and they won the game.

Score _____ (Top Score 10)    Vocabulary for Debate • Build New Vocabulary

 **Word Play**

## Crossword Puzzle

 Choose a vocabulary word to answer each clue below. Write the vocabulary word in the squares to solve the crossword puzzle.

**ACROSS**

3. An antonym of "to agree with"
6. If you work something out, you come up with a _____.
7. To annoy or bother
8. A synonym of *scheme*
9. "I never asked for your _____!"
10. A strong belief

**DOWN**

1. A synonym of *disgusting*
2. "I will _____ you to change your mind."
4. Rhymes with *massive*
5. To boldly face

1. **charity**
(char´ i tē) *n.*
an organization that
helps the poor

2. **privacy**
(prī´ və sē) *n.*
the state of being alone

3. **granary**
(grā´ nə rē) *n.*
a place for storing grain

4. **gallery**
(gal´ ə rē) *n.*
a place where art
is shown

5. **galaxy**
(gal´ ək sē) *n.*
a large grouping
of stars

6. **economy**
(i kon´ ə mē) *n.*
a system of managing
money

7. **dynasty**
(dī´ nə stē) *n.*
a line of rulers from
a family

8. **inquiry**
(in kwīr´ ē) *n.*
a question

9. **dignitary**
(dig´ ni ter´ ē) *n.*
a government official

10. **necessity**
(ni ses´ i tē) *n.*
something needed

# Nouns Ending in y

## (1) Word Meanings

## Context Clues and Definitions

Read the sentences below. Choose the vocabulary word
that best completes each sentence, and write it in the
blank.

1. Goods and services, as well as buying and selling, are
important parts of the _____.

2. When you choose not to share information about yourself,
you want your _____.

3. An excellent place to see an art collection is in a
_____.

4. An organization that collects money or items for a helpful
cause is a _____.

5. When you ask questions about something, you make an
_____.

6. Something you must have is considered to be a
_____.

7. A place where grain is stored is a _____.

8. A _____ is a very important official.

9. A group of stars and planets held together by gravity is a
_____.

10. A long line of rulers from the same family is called a
_____.

## ② Reference Skills

# Elements of a Definition

 Read each vocabulary word below, and use a dictionary to look up their extended definitions. Complete the chart by circling the best answer for each of the categories of definition elements.

| Vocabulary Word | Category (What Is It?) | Characteristic (What Is It Like?) | Example |
|---|---|---|---|
| 1. charity | organization<br>equipment | helps people in need<br>has an alarm | department store<br>food pantry |
| 2. dignitary | type of plant<br>a person | high position<br>fruit | The Pope<br>school teacher |
| 3. galaxy | universe<br>beverages | group of stars<br>refreshing | orange juice<br>Milky Way |
| 4. gallery | a place<br>a book | used for reference<br>contains artwork | museum<br>dictionary |
| 5. dynasty | detergent<br>heritage | rulers<br>lemony fresh smell | Super Clean<br>Egypt's Pharaonic |
| 6. granary | person<br>structure | stores grains<br>serves dinner | a glass bowl<br>barn |

 **Think About It**

Knowing some or all of the elements of a definition can strengthen your word knowledge and help you use words correctly in context.

## Vocabulary List

1. charity

2. privacy

3. granary

4. gallery

5. galaxy

6. economy

7. dynasty

8. inquiry

9. dignitary

10. necessity

# 3 Build New Vocabulary

## Plurals

  Write the plural of each of the vocabulary words in alphabetical order. You will need to change the *y* to *i* and add *es* for each word.

1. _____    6. _____

2. _____    7. _____

3. _____    8. _____

4. _____    9. _____

5. _____    10. _____

Now make the following words plural by adding *s* or *es*. Check your spelling in a dictionary.

11. valley _____

12. velocity _____

13. reality _____

14. donkey _____

15. pass _____

16. juice _____

17. candle _____

18. potato _____

19. province _____

20. subway _____

  **Word Play**

## Help Wanted!

Complete the job advertisement below using the vocabulary words. (**Hint:** One of the words you use will need to be made plural.)

# HELP WANTED!

One well-known, intelligent, and charming _____ to replace the current ruler of a distinguished

_____. Knowledge of how to keep the

_____ growing strong by providing jobs and production of goods and services is an absolute

_____. You will have very little

_____, so you must be an outgoing person. A

history of working with a _____ as a volunteer

is a plus. Only human beings from this _____ need apply. No one from outer space, please. Send all

_____ to Emanuel Trust, 300 Peoples Street, Washington, D.C., 20001.

# Vocabulary Review

## 1 Review Word Meanings

Read the passage below. Then answer the questions about the boldfaced vocabulary words.

### Unspoken Communication

Communication is important. There are many ways to communicate. We send and receive information verbally and through our actions. Some people **transmit** information about how they are feeling without realizing they are doing it. A big smile and bright, shining eyes can mean that someone is feeling **ecstatic.** A red face and an angry glare warn people that the person is feeling angry. An unwillingness to look another person in the eye can indicate **shame.** A deep sigh informs a listener that a person is **wistful,** whereas a shrug of the shoulders might mean he or she is **indifferent.**

How would a man who is **nauseated** look? He would probably have a strange look on his face and might even be holding his stomach. That is a message you wouldn't want to misunderstand! What other actions **inform** you of how someone is feeling?

What is the intention of a woman who is standing with her feet spread apart, her hands on her hips, and a scowl on her face? If you think that person might be ready to **confront** you about a problem, you are probably right. What about someone who looks lost or confused and comes to you with a question in his or her eyes? That person is probably going to make an **inquiry.** Understanding communication, through actions as well as through words, is important.

...........................................................................................................

Now read the following questions. Then completely fill in the bubble of the correct answer.

1. *Answer* is to *reply* as *ask* is to _____.
   Ⓐ recommend
   Ⓑ inform
   Ⓒ inquiry

2. Which of the following words means "to make someone aware"?
   Ⓐ wistful
   Ⓑ inform
   Ⓒ inquiry

3. Which of the following words is an antonym for *shame?*
   Ⓐ pride
   Ⓑ guilt
   Ⓒ embarrassment

4. Which sentence below includes the correct definition for *indifferent?*
   Ⓐ When you have an interest in something, you are indifferent.
   Ⓑ When you have no feeling toward something, you are indifferent.
   Ⓒ When you dislike something very much, you are indifferent.

## ② Review Word Meanings

Read the passage below. Then answer the questions about the boldfaced vocabulary words.

# Written Communication

Written communication can be timeless. Writers share their thoughts through articles, books, journals, stories, and letters. For a **minimum** expense, letters are a great way to **correspond.** There are several different kinds of letters that serve different purposes. A letter to the editor can be used to inform people of things that are going on in the community; to **request** help from a lot of people, such as volunteers to clean up a **vacant** lot in the neighborhood; or to express your **opinion** and hopefully **persuade** others to feel the same.

A friendly letter can be used to stay in touch with pen pals in **remote** areas of the world or even someone in a different **section** of the same town you live in. A business letter can serve as a good tool for you to use when you wish to express your concern to a **dignitary** over some issue, such as the **economy.** If you have a **dispute** with a business, such as being **irked** by **offensive** service or tricked by someone posing as a **charity** worker, you can write a business letter to seek a **resolution** to the problem. Sending a letter allows you to express yourself and, hopefully, get a helpful **reply** in return.

Now read the following questions. Then completely fill in the bubble of the correct answer.

1. Which meaning for *remote* is used in the passage above?
   Ⓐ a control used to operate something from a distance
   Ⓑ located at a distance; not near
   Ⓒ small in degree; faint or slight

2. Which of the following pairs represents a synonym and an antonym for *offensive?*
   Ⓐ disgusting/pleasing
   Ⓑ repulsive/disagreeable
   Ⓒ polite/pleasant

3. Which phonetic spelling for *charity* is correct?
   Ⓐ cha′ rā ty
   Ⓑ chōr ri tē
   Ⓒ char′ i tē

4. Which of the following statements is true according to the passage above?
   Ⓐ Letters are an expensive way to communicate.
   Ⓑ Written communication can be timeless.
   Ⓒ A friendly letter is an old way of keeping in touch with people around the world.

5. Which of the following is a synonym for *irked?*
   Ⓐ upset
   Ⓑ hungry
   Ⓒ sad

## 3 Review Word Meanings

Read the passage below. Then answer the questions about the boldfaced vocabulary words.

# Signs of the Times

For many years pictures, signs, and symbols have been important forms of communication. Paintings and photographs in art **galleries** provide history and communication from artists of the past and present. Symbols on badges or medals, such as those worn by the military or officials in ancient Chinese **dynasties,** tell the rank or importance of the person who wore them.

Signs are more important now than ever before. Signs you might be familiar with include a **minus** sign used in math and a question mark at the end of a sentence, indicating an inquiry. More recently, lasers have been used as signs and have been **projected** into the sky or onto buildings to send messages or to entertain.

The demand for signs with pictures and symbols is growing. Easy-to-read road signs are a **necessity.** Have you ever seen the sign with a swirl on a square? It tells drivers which roads they should use when they must **evacuate** an area quickly, such as when a hurricane is moving in. A big plus symbol on a sign indicates that two roads **intersect** ahead. One can only imagine signs that might be needed in the future. How about a sign showing the direction to the Milky Way **galaxy?**

Now read the following questions. Then completely fill in the bubble of the correct answer.

1. Which of the following words is the plural form of *galaxy?*
   - Ⓐ galaxys
   - Ⓑ galaxies
   - Ⓒ galasies

2. Which of the following words is not an example of a *necessity?*
   - Ⓐ sleep
   - Ⓑ water
   - Ⓒ accessories

3. Which of the following examples is a synonym for *intersect?*
   - Ⓐ cross
   - Ⓑ side by side
   - Ⓒ go around

4. In which sentence below is the correct definition for *dynasty* given?
   - Ⓐ The last Chinese dynasty, ruled by one family for more than 200 years, was the Qing dynasty.
   - Ⓑ The last Chinese dynasty, and a strong one, was the Qing dynasty.
   - Ⓒ The last Chinese dynasty, which was in Mongolia, was the Qing dynasty.

5. Which word below contains a Latin root that means "small" or "less"?
   - Ⓐ projected
   - Ⓑ minus
   - Ⓒ inquiry

# 4 Review Word Meanings

Read the passage below. Then answer the questions about the boldfaced vocabulary words.

## Anne Sullivan and Helen Keller

If you wonder whether communication is a **necessity** for humans, consider the story of Helen Keller and Anne Sullivan. At 19 months old, an illness left Helen Keller unable to see, hear, or speak. Instead of becoming a **passive** child, she became uncontrollable. She was very angry and seemed to **despise** everything and everyone. Anne Sullivan, legally blind herself, must have been **appalled** at the behavior she first witnessed, but Anne arrived at Helen's home with the **conviction** that she could help her. This would prove to be a major, not a **minor,** task.

First Anne had to get Helen to obey her. She needed to find a way to communicate with Helen. Anne used her fingers to spell words into Helen's hand. After about a month, Helen caught on. Helen finally connected the feel of water to W-A-T-E-R. Helen learned quickly and even went on to learn phrases in different languages, which she **injected** into the many letters she wrote to friends and dignitaries around the world. Helen opened her life to others so that they, too, might have a better life.

When Helen wanted **privacy,** she spent time at her home, Arcan Ridge. Anne Sullivan was very proud and never **jealous** of all that Helen was able to accomplish.

Now read the following questions. Then completely fill in the bubble of the correct answer.

1. Which of the following is not a definition for *minor?*
   Ⓐ under legal age
   Ⓑ not as important
   Ⓒ one who mines

2. Which sentence below includes the definition for *privacy?*
   Ⓐ Helen wanted privacy occasionally.
   Ⓑ When Helen wanted privacy, or to be alone, she stopped traveling.
   Ⓒ Helen enjoyed her privacy at her home in Connecticut.

3. Which of the following is a pair of antonyms?
   Ⓐ despise/love
   Ⓑ despise/hate
   Ⓒ despise/fear

4. Which of the following words can be made plural?
   Ⓐ dignitary
   Ⓑ jealous
   Ⓒ inject

5. Which of the following words means "the judgment that one is guilty of a crime" or "a strong belief."
   Ⓐ conviction
   Ⓑ necessity
   Ⓒ privacy

1. **declaration**
(dek´ lə rā´ shən) *n.*
a formal statement

2. **capsize**
(kap´ sīz) *v.*
to turn over

3. **homestead**
(hōm´ sted) *n.*
a house and its land

4. **opportunity**
(op´ ər tōo´ ni tē) *n.*
a timely event

5. **persist**
(pər sist´) *v.*
to keep going

6. **obstacle**
(ob´ stə kəl) *n.*
something in the
way of progress

7. **protest**
(prō´ test) *v.*
to express
disapproval

8. **survey**
(sər vā´) *v.*
to look at as a
whole

9. **prevail**
(pri vāl´) *v.*
to win

10. **territory**
(ter´ i tor´ ē) *n.*
a large area of land

# A Changing America

## ① Word Meanings

### Memory Tools

 Use the underlined words as memory tools to help you choose each vocabulary word described below.

1. If you think of a <u>cap</u>, it looks like a boat in this condition. _____

2. If you have not prepared for a <u>test</u>, you may do this when the time comes to take it. _____

3. A pioneer would have built a <u>home</u> on this.

   _____

4. <u>Clara</u> made this to tell us that she will be moving to the West in less than a month. _____

5. You will <u>ail</u> if your health does not do this.

   _____

6. Colonists did not want a <u>Tory</u> in this land that belonged to them. _____

7. Now would be a good time to <u>tune</u> my guitar.

   _____

8. Your <u>sis</u> will be angry if you do this while teasing her.

   _____

9. It would <u>serve</u> you well to do this when you enter a room.

   _____

10. Some people like to <u>tackle</u> difficult tasks.

    _____

## ② Reference Skills

# Using a Dictionary

Place a check mark in the box of the sentence that uses each underlined vocabulary word correctly.

1. ☐ The soldier said, "General Washington, you must sit down before you capsize the boat."

   ☐ The soldier must capsize his supplies, or he will surely run out.

2. ☐ Betsy Ross made the first American flag out of woven protest.

   ☐ The Boston Tea Party was a protest against unfair taxes.

3. ☐ My great, great grandfather claimed a 100-acre homestead in 1832.

   ☐ Her homestead came to fix the leaking kitchen sink.

4. ☐ The steamship smoothly sailed up the territory.

   ☐ The territory explored by Lewis and Clark was called the Louisiana Purchase.

5. ☐ Patrick Henry made the declaration, "Give me liberty or give me death."

   ☐ The declaration was pulled by six white horses.

6. ☐ Be careful not to drop the obstacles because they may shatter.

   ☐ Poor roads were big obstacles for homesteaders.

7. ☐ The homesteader stood at the top of the hill to survey all of her land.

   ☐ Did you survey a large meal to the president and his family?

8. ☐ Pioneers had to be strong and determined to persist toward their goal of finding a better life.

   ☐ If I cannot persist you to join me, then I will just go alone.

A Changing America • Reference Skills         Score _____ (Top Score 8)        Unit 6 • Lesson 31    **123**

## Vocabulary List

1. declaration
2. capsize
3. homestead
4. opportunity
5. persist
6. obstacle
7. protest
8. survey
9. prevail
10. territory

# 3 Build New Vocabulary

## Using Synonyms in Context

 Read the sentences below. Circle the vocabulary word in parentheses that could take the place of the boldfaced synonym in each sentence. Use a dictionary to define unknown words.

1. The investigator will **examine** the crime scene. *(protest/survey)*

2. I promise to **persevere** until I succeed. *(persist/capsize)*

3. This party is a good **occasion** to meet new people. *(obstacle/opportunity)*

4. We saw the entire **region** from the peak of the mountain. *(declaration/territory)*

5. Our canoe will **turn over** if you are not careful getting in. *(protest/capsize)*

6. My mother drove around the **barricade** in the road. *(obstacle/homestead)*

7. Mary read the **document** stating that bringing a lamb to school was against the rules. *(territory/declaration)*

8. She **cried out,** "Why can't I bring my lamb to school?" *(protest/survey)*

9. "Will justice ever **triumph?**" Mary wondered. *(persist/prevail)*

10. In 1930, Sarah Hale wrote the nursery rhyme about Mary Sawyer and her lamb, whose **residence** was in Sterling, Massachusetts. *(homestead/opportunity)*

 **Word Play**

## Rebus Equations

 Solve the rebus equations below to find each hidden vocabulary word. Write the vocabulary word in the blank.

1.  + 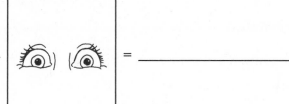 = _____

2.  + ist = _____

3. pre + 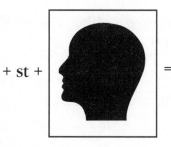 = _____

4.  + st +  = _____

## Vocabulary List

1. **fortress**
   (for´ tris) *n.*
   a protected place

2. **temple**
   (tem´ pəl) *n.*
   a building used
   for worship

3. **document**
   (dok´ yə mənt) *n.*
   written information

4. **chariot**
   (char´ ē ət) *n.*
   a vehicle pulled by
   horses

5. **pyramid**
   (pir´ ə mid´) *n.*
   a stone structure
   used as a tomb

6. **peasant**
   (pez´ ənt) *n.*
   a farm worker

7. **crusade**
   (kroō sād´) *n.*
   a movement
   against evil

8. **interpret**
   (in tər´ prit) *v.*
   to explain

9. **decline**
   (di klīn´) *n.*
   a weakening

10. **salvage**
    (sal´ vij) *v.*
    to save

# Vocabulary for History

 **Word Meanings**

## Word Choice

 Circle the vocabulary word in parentheses that best completes each sentence below.

1. The new governor promised a *(peasant/crusade)* against crime in her state.

2. She provided an official *(salvage/document)* from her bag as proof.

3. Many people wonder what caused the *(decline/chariot)* of the great Roman Empire.

4. The Great *(Interpret/Pyramid)* of Khufu was built by an Egyptian pharaoh to serve as a tomb when he died.

5. A building used for worship is called a *(temple/fortress)*.

6. We needed her to *(decline/interpret)* what the man was saying for us because we did not speak his language.

7. The troops stood guard and were ready to defend the *(fortress/salvage)*.

8. A vehicle used by many people in the past was called a *(crusade/chariot)*.

9. He was a *(temple/peasant)* like his family who had worked on the farm for generations.

10. After the fire, the girl was able to *(pyramid/salvage)* what was left of her china doll collection.

## Reference Skills

# Word Origins

Read the word origin entries below. Decide which vocabulary word best matches each entry and write it in the blank.

1. from Latin *documentum,* meaning "official paper"

   _____

2. from Old French *chariotte,* meaning "car"

   _____

3. from Old French *salver,* meaning "to save"

   _____

4. from Old French *forteresse,* meaning "strong place"

   _____

5. from Latin *pagus,* meaning "rural district"

   _____

6. from Latin *interpretari,* meaning "explain; understand"

   _____

7. from Latin *templum,* meaning "building for worship"

   _____

8. from Latin *declinare,* meaning "to bend from; to turn aside" _____

9. from Latin *pyramis,* meaning "one of the pyramids of Egypt" _____

10. from Latin *crux,* meaning "cross"

    _____

## Vocabulary List

1. fortress
2. temple
3. document
4. chariot
5. pyramid
6. peasant
7. crusade
8. interpret
9. decline
10. salvage

# 3 Build New Vocabulary

## Context Clues

 Read the sentences below. Use context clues to choose the vocabulary word that best completes each sentence. Write the vocabulary word in the blank.

1. Two, very fast horses pulled the _____, a vehicle used for racing, around the ring in the Hippodrome.

2. The life of a _____, a farmer in the Middle Ages, was a difficult one.

3. Many important artifacts have been found buried with

   mummies in _____, or Egyptian tombs.

4. It takes great skill to read, _____, and preserve ancient Egyptian hieroglyphs.

5. Dr. Martin Luther King, Jr. launched a _____, or movement, against injustice.

6. The Middle Ages began after the _____ and fall of the Roman Empire.

7. Archaeologists are scientists who search for, discover, and

   carefully _____, or save, ancient artifacts.

8. The Declaration of Independence is an important

   historical _____, or written piece of information.

9. One must show respect in a place of worship, or a

   _____.

10. The Tower of London is an ancient _____, a strong and safe building, built by William the Conqueror in 1078.

Score _____ (Top Score 10)   Vocabulary for History • Build New Vocabulary

# Word Play

## Word Detective

 Read the clues below to determine which vocabulary word is being described. Write the vocabulary word in the blank.

1. I was history's version of the modern-day race-car. I was

   pulled by horses. What am I? _____

2. I worked hard with little chance for a better life in medieval times. I often came home dirty, hot, and tired at the end of a long day in the fields. Who am I?

   _____

3. Whether artifacts are at the bottom of the ocean or in an ancient buried city, this can sometimes be done to keep them for future generations. What is this called?

   _____

4. I am the only one of the Seven Wonders of the Ancient World that is still standing. Many others were also built to hold Egyptian kings' bodies when they died. What am I?

   _____

5. I am an official piece of written information, such as your birth certificate or even the Declaration of Independence.

   What am I? _____

6. I am a building that often gives protection against enemies. You might find weapons and soldiers in me.

   What am I? _____

7. I am a movement started to fight against something

   believed to be evil. What am I? _____

8. I am a place designed for people to come and show their respect for who or what they believe in. What am I?

   _____

**Vocabulary List**

1. **urban**
   (ûr´ bən) *adj.*
   relating to a city

2. **suburban**
   (sə bûr´ bən) *adj.*
   relating to the area
   just outside a city

3. **rural**
   (rûr´ əl) *adj.*
   relating to the
   country

4. **sanctuary**
   (sangk´ chōō er´ ē) *n.*
   a place of protection

5. **glen**
   (glen) *n.*
   a small valley

6. **cavern**
   (kav´ ərn) *n.*
   an underground cave

7. **dune**
   (dōōn) *n.*
   hill or ridge of sand

8. **hemisphere**
   (hem´ i sfir´) *n.*
   one half of Earth

9. **wasteland**
   (wāst´ land´) *n.*
   an area with few or
   no living things

10. **marsh**
    (märsh) *n.*
    a low, wet land

# Lands and Regions

**1** **Word Meanings**

## Classifying

 Read the sets of examples below. Choose the vocabulary word that best classifies each set. Write the vocabulary word in the blank.

1. city, metropolitan, skyscrapers _____

2. protection, shelter, place _____

3. sand, hill, desert _____

4. no life, area of land, barren _____

5. wet, wildlife habitat, swampy _____

6. glacier-formed, valley, Scotland _____

7. community, outside of the city, not in the country

   _____

8. equator, half, Greenwich meridian _____

9. hollow, cave, damp _____

10. spread out, country, farming _____

## 2  Reference Skills

# Antonyms and Synonyms

 Read the sentences below. Choose the vocabulary word that is an antonym or a synonym of the underlined word in each sentence. Write the vocabulary word in the blank and circle *Antonym* or *Synonym* to tell how it is being used.

1. The birdwatchers found a family of whooping cranes living in the

   <u>swamp</u>. _____      Antonym      Synonym

2. After living in the country all his life, Kenji was excited see new things at the <u>rural</u> college.      Antonym      Synonym

   _____

3. The path led us deep into the narrow <u>peak</u> where mountains surrounded us on both sides.      Antonym      Synonym

   _____

4. The San Diego Wild Animal Park is a safe <u>haven</u> for the White Rhinoceros as it battles extinction.      Antonym      Synonym

   _____

5. If nothing is growing in this particular area, you might be in

   a <u>desert</u>. _____      Antonym      Synonym

• • • • • • • • • • • • • • • • • • • • • • • • • • • • • • • • • •

## Think About It

Learning new words and how they relate to words that you already know can help you remember how to use them. Knowing how to use new words correctly also gives you a bigger and better vocabulary.

**Vocabulary List**

| |
|---|
| **1.** *urban* |
| **2.** *suburban* |
| **3.** *rural* |
| **4.** *sanctuary* |
| **5.** *glen* |
| **6.** *cavern* |
| **7.** *dune* |
| **8.** *hemisphere* |
| **9.** *wasteland* |
| **10.** *marsh* |

 **3** **Build New Vocabulary**

## Word Parts

 Read the word parts and their meanings below. Then write the vocabulary word that is made from the sum of the word parts given.

| **Prefix** | **Root** | **Suffix** |
|---|---|---|
| **1.** none | *urb:* "city" | *-an:* "relating to" |

**Word** _____

| **Prefix** | **Root** | **Suffix** |
|---|---|---|
| **2.** *sub-:* "secondary" | *urb:* "city" | *-an:* "relating to" |

**Word** _____

• • • • • • • • • • • • • • • • • • • • • • • • • • • • • • • • • •

 Now solve the following word part equations to form new words.

**3.** *sub- + ject =* _____

**4.** *in- + ject + -or =* _____

**5.** *in- + ject + -ion =* _____

**6.** *sub- + sect + -ion =* _____

• • • • • • • • • • • • • • • • • • • • • • • • • • • • • • • • • •

Use the words you formed in the exercises above to complete the sentences below.

**7.** Math is my favorite _____.

**8.** In the book about reptiles, there was a _____ about iguanas.

**9.** The nurse said I was going to get an _____.

**10.** _____ families have many museums, stores, and theaters close to their homes.

# Word Play

## Puns

 Read each pun below. Use words from the box to complete each answer. Write the word in the blank.

| | | | |
|---|---|---|---|
| wasteland | despair | dune | rural |
| abundance | marsh | seldom | adobe |

1. What did one grain of sand say to the others?

   Answer: What are you _____ here?

2. What did the city mouse say to the country mouse when he visited?

   Answer: It is _____ peaceful here.

3. How do wetland creatures move from place to place?

   Answer: They _____. Hup, two, three, four.

4. Where does Mother Nature have to take in her pants when she loses weight?

   Answer: Around her _____.

5. What did the tired clerk in the shoe department say to the fussy customer as she tried on the fifteenth pair of shoes?

   Answer: Are you sure you don't like _____?

6. What does a happy roll do when it hears a catchy tune?

   Answer: _____

7. What did the ticket dealer say when he had extra tickets?

   Answer: I must try harder to _____ tickets!

8. What do you call a loaf of bread that makes its own honey?

   Answer: _____

## Vocabulary List

1. **suspend**
   (sə spend') v.
   to hold in one place

2. **shrug**
   (shrug) v.
   to raise the shoulders

3. **pluck**
   (pluk) v.
   to pull out

4. **struggle**
   (strug' əl) v.
   to work hard

5. **stalk**
   (stôk) v.
   to track down

6. **shrivel**
   (shriv' əl) v.
   to shrink and become wrinkled

7. **quiver**
   (kwi' vər) v.
   to shake slightly

8. **crouch**
   (krouch) v.
   to bend low

9. **surge**
   (sûrj) v.
   to swell and move forward

10. **plod**
    (plod) v.
    to move slowly and heavily

# "Actions" Vocabulary

## 1 Word Meanings

### Words in Action

 Write the vocabulary word that is being described in each sentence. Use the underlined clues for help.

1. The tiger will <u>bend low</u> in the tall grass to watch its prey.
   _____

2. Wolves silently <u>hunt and track down</u> other animals by placing their back feet in the same spot as their front feet.
   _____

3. Hummingbirds can <u>stay in one place</u> in midair to feed on the nectar of a blossoming flower. _____

4. The Galápagos Tortoise <u>moves slowly and heavily</u> along the hot, dry land of South America. _____

5. The bird-cage plant grows on desert sand dunes. When the dunes move, the roots <u>shrink and become wrinkled</u>.
   _____

6. Wild dogs <u>put forth great effort</u> to decide who will become the leader of the pack. _____

7. The male gorilla will often <u>raise up his shoulders</u> to the female when she is nursing her young. _____

8. The puffer fish will <u>swell and move forward</u> to protect itself from being eaten by other fish. _____

9. Some parrots will <u>pull out</u> their own feathers in response to being bored. _____

10. The mouse backed into the corner and began to <u>shake slightly</u> when it heard footsteps. _____

## 2 Reference Skills

# Guide Words

 Read each set of guide words below. Choose the vocabulary word you would find on the page between each set of guide words and write it in the blank.

**Guide Words**

1. seldom/shrubbery _____

2. structure/suburban _____

3. crocodile/crowd _____

4. plow/quilt _____

5. survivor/swan _____

6. stadium/strawberry _____

7. obedient/plot _____

8. quit/region _____

9. superstar/survive _____

10. shroud/sound _____

• • • • • • • • • • • • • • • • • • • • • • • • • • • • • • • • • • • • • • • •

Match the vocabulary words below with their definitions.

11. _____ quiver        **A.** to increase and move forward

12. _____ struggle      **B.** to stoop or bend low

13. _____ plod          **C.** to make a great effort

14. _____ shrug         **D.** to shrink and become wrinkled

15. _____ surge         **E.** to move slowly and heavily

16. _____ pluck         **F.** to shake slightly; tremble

17. _____ shrivel       **G.** to pull out or off; pick

18. _____ crouch        **H.** to raise the shoulders

## Vocabulary List

1. suspend
2. shrug
3. pluck
4. struggle
5. stalk
6. shrivel
7. quiver
8. crouch
9. surge
10. plod

# 3 Build New Vocabulary

## Past Tense

Each sentence below is written in the present tense. Change the boldfaced vocabulary word so that it is in the past tense and write it in the blank.

1. Kevin **suspends** the food high in a tree away from the

   bears and raccoons. _____

2. Eve **plucks** her guitar after dark on the porch.

   _____

3. Julio's energy **surges** close to the finish line.

   _____

4. Caleb **plods** through his daily routine, wishing for
   something exciting to happen.

   _____

5. The hungry cat **stalks** the worried mouse.

   _____

6. The grapes **shrivel** in the sun.

   _____

7. Shy Angela **shrugs** her shoulders instead of answering.

   _____

8. Aniela **crouches** behind the couch, hoping to scare her
   brother.

   _____

9. The fish **struggles** to get off the hook.

   _____

10. Joyce **quivers** while waiting for the spelling bee to begin.

    _____

Score _____ (Top Score 10)   "Actions" Vocabulary • Build New Vocabulary

# 4 Word Play

## Onomatopoeia

 Read the sentences below, and pay close attention to how the boldfaced vocabulary words are used. Then choose an onomatopoeic word from the box that best matches each sentence and write it in the blank.

| twang | slurped | creak |
|-------|---------|-------|
| Burr  | grunted | howl  |

1. As her lips began to **quiver** and her body began to shake,

   Linda complained, "_____! It is freezing out here!"

2. The country singer **plucked** his guitar string, and it broke

   with a _____.

3. The woods were quiet, except for the _____ of the wind through the trees as the bobcat silently **stalked** his prey.

4. Its footsteps _____ in the mud as the slow-moving elephant **plodded** along the path in the rain.

5. The young calf _____ as he **struggled** to walk for the first time.

6. We could hear the old, wooden roller coaster

   _____ while we were **suspended** at the top of the hill.

1. **ebb**
   (eb) *n.*
   the flow of the tide
   from shore

2. **tidewater**
   (tīd′ wô tər) *n.*
   water brought up
   by the tide

3. **gull**
   (gul) *n.*
   a bird found near
   the sea

4. **scorch**
   (skorch) *v.*
   to burn slightly

5. **visor**
   (vī′ zər) *n.*
   the brim of a cap

6. **pier**
   (pir) *n.*
   a landing place
   for boats

7. **maroon**
   (mə rōōn′) *v.*
   to leave alone

8. **lounge**
   (lounj) *v.*
   to sit or lie lazily

9. **aqua**
   (ä′ kwə) *n.*
   a greenish blue color

10. **crest**
    (krest) *n.*
    the highest point

# On the Beach

## 1 Word Meanings

### Concept Words

 Read each set of concept words below. Choose the vocabulary word that best relates to each set and write it in the blank.

1. hill, ridge, wave, surfer _____

2. water, blue, color, sky _____

3. tide, movement, away, water _____

4. island, alone, shipwreck, despair

   _____

5. sunshine, cap, shield, sight _____

6. feathers, shore, water, shriek _____

7. floods, seacoast, lowlands, changing

   _____

8. sunbathe, read, relax, recline _____

9. skin, burn, danger, sunscreen _____

10. dock, boats, landing, wharf _____

• • • • • • • • • • • • • • • • • • • • • • • • • • • • • • • •

### Think About It

Categorizing new words into already known concepts will help you remember how to properly use them. Can you think of more concept words for each vocabulary word in addition to those listed above?

## 2 Reference Skills

# Words With More Than One Meaning

 Look up each underlined word in a dictionary. Write the definition of the word as it is used in the sentence.

**1.** Augustine loved her new <u>maroon</u> coat.

_____

**2.** The cockatoo raised its <u>crest</u> to get attention.

_____

**3.** The driver put the <u>visor</u> down to shield his eyes.

_____

**4.** You will <u>scorch</u> that shirt if the iron is too hot.

_____

Draw a check mark in the box before the sentence that uses the word in a way that best matches its definition.

**5.** *maroon:* to abandon or leave helpless

☐ The bright red umbrella looked <u>maroon</u> when it was wet.

☐ He was <u>marooned</u> on an island for years.

**6.** *crest:* highest point

☐ The family <u>crest</u> was displayed above the doorway.

☐ The surfer reached the <u>crest</u> of the wave.

**7.** *lounge:* a public waiting room

☐ We will meet in the <u>lounge</u> after school.

☐ They decided to <u>lounge</u> for a while after exercising.

**8.** *ebb:* to become less or weaker

☐ The <u>ebb</u> of the tide took our toys out to sea.

☐ Her fame as an actor has begun to <u>ebb</u>.

## Vocabulary List

1. ebb

2. tidewater

3. gull

4. scorch

5. visor

6. pier

7. maroon

8. lounge

9. aqua

10. crest

# 3 Build New Vocabulary

## Root Words

 The Latin root *aqua* means "water." Each word below contains the root *aqua*. Look up each word in a dictionary and write its definition in the blank.

1. *aquarium:* _____

_____

_____

2. *aquatic:* _____

_____

_____

3. *aquamarine:* _____

_____

_____

4. *aquaplane:* _____

_____

_____

5. *aquanaut:* _____

_____

_____

• • • • • • • • • • • • • • • • • • • • • • • • • • • • • • • • • • • • •

 Now complete each sentence below using the new words from above.

6. Clean your _____ once in a while to keep the fish healthy.

7. The _____ discovered a new kind of squid.

8. The birthstone for March is the _____.

# Word Play

## Name Another

Read the rhymes below. Choose the word from the box that best completes each rhyme and write it in the blank. (**Hint:** The boldfaced vocabulary words and clues in parentheses will help you.)

| | | |
|---|---|---|
| moon | stranded | pelican |
| slouch | peak | shades |

1. When you're relaxing on the sand, you might see a **gull** or

   a _____ (another sea bird).

2. To **lounge** is to lie around, to bend down is to crouch, and

   to not stand up straight—we call that a _____
   (another body position).

3. "**Tidewater** is affected by gravity," said June. Then she

   explained how it relates to the _____ (another
   word connected to the rising and falling of the tide).

4. It's the highest point of the mountain we seek. Some call it

   the **crest;** we'll call it the _____ (another
   name for the highest point).

5. My new **visor** won't fit because of my braids, so today I

   guess I will just wear my _____ (another
   accessory used to see better in the bright sun).

6. Poor, old Albert was **marooned** when his plane finally

   landed. On a small deserted island, for years he was

   _____ (another word meaning "to be left

   helplessly").

# Vocabulary Review

## 1 Review Word Meanings

Read the passage below. Then answer the questions about the boldfaced vocabulary words.

## A Need for Change

Freedom has been a driving force for human beings for a long time. Throughout history, people have **crusaded** for freedom. However, people **interpret** freedom in different ways. It can mean choosing how to worship, obtaining land and possessions, or being treated with respect no matter who you are or what you are.

Nearly four hundred years ago, the Pilgrims **struggled** for the freedom to worship as they saw fit. In a **protest** against the King of England, a group known as the "Saints" moved to Holland. They later decided that a better life awaited them in the New World. Before their voyage even began, they overcame many **obstacles,** such as getting money to pay for a ship and supplies. The Pilgrims **persisted** and in September 1620, their journey began.

The Pilgrims were not sailors. They were sick, and they probably worried that the *Mayflower* would **capsize** in the rough waters. The ship was crowded with more than 130 people, at least two dogs, and a cat. (After all, something had to **stalk** the rats!) Sixty days later, while **surveying** the ocean, someone shouted that they could see land. A new life was about to begin.

. . . . . . . . . . . . . . . . . . . . . . . . . . . . . . . . . . . . . . . . . . . . . . . . . . . . . . . . . . . . . . . . . . . . . . . . . . . . . . .

Now read the following questions. Then completely fill in the bubble of the correct answer.

1. Which of the following is the best word choice for "looking over"?
   Ⓐ struggling
   Ⓑ crusading
   Ⓒ surveying

2. Which action word best describes the underlined phrase in the following sentence?
   The cat will <u>hunt or track down</u> the mice on the ship.
   Ⓐ interpret
   Ⓑ stalk
   Ⓒ protest

3. Which word belongs with the following concept words?
   *strong, driven, dedicated*
   Ⓐ persisted
   Ⓑ horizon
   Ⓒ capsize

4. Which statement is true according to the passage above?
   Ⓐ Throughout history people have protested against freedom.
   Ⓑ The Pilgrims began their journey to the New World in September, 1620.
   Ⓒ All of the Pilgrims were professionel sailors.

## ❷ Review Word Meanings

Read the passage below. Then answer the questions about the boldfaced vocabulary words.

# Life in the New World

This new **territory** held the promise of a better life for the Pilgrims. However, even before they got off the *Mayflower,* the Pilgrims realized they needed rules to live by in this new place. For this purpose, they created a **document** called the Mayflower Compact. After finding a good place to live, the Pilgrims started to build. They started with the Common House, but often had to **suspend** building because the weather got too bad. Eventually the Pilgrims built a **fortress** at the **crest** of the hill. This was truly a **sanctuary** because they used it as a lookout and as a place of worship. Unfortunately, that first winter was hard. People's health **declined** due to sickness, cold, and hunger. Half of the Pilgrims died by spring.

In the spring, building and planting continued. Even though the work was hard and many of them had **scorched** faces from long hours of working in the sun, the Pilgrim spirit **prevailed.**

At harvest, Governor Bradford made a **declaration** that a celebration was in order. The Pilgrims invited their Native American friends to eat and give thanks for all they had. As you know, this was the first Thanksgiving.

Now read the following questions. Then completely fill in the bubble of the correct answer.

1. An antonym for *improved* is _____.
   - Ⓐ declined
   - Ⓑ prevailed
   - Ⓒ scorched

2. A synonym for *burned* is _____.
   - Ⓐ suspended
   - Ⓑ scorched
   - Ⓒ prevailed

3. Between which set of guide words would you find *sanctuary?*
   - Ⓐ salvage/sample
   - Ⓑ sandwich/Saturn
   - Ⓒ samurai/sandal

4. The captain made a formal statement, or _____, saying that everyone was free to worship as he or she saw fit.
   - Ⓐ fortress
   - Ⓑ sanctuary
   - Ⓒ declaration

5. Between which set of guide words would you find *suspend?*
   - Ⓐ spend/suspect
   - Ⓑ steamboat/suspense
   - Ⓒ swan/syllable

6. Which vocabulary word comes from the Old French *forteresse,* meaning "strong place"?
   - Ⓐ fortress
   - Ⓑ territory
   - Ⓒ protest

## 3 Review Word Meanings

Read the passage below. Then answer the questions about the boldfaced vocabulary words.

# Moving Westward

During the 1800s, land prices in the East rose, and people heard that they could have a better life if they moved west. **Quivering** with hope and longing for a **homestead** of their own on enough land to farm, pioneer families packed a few belongings into covered wagons and set out. The journey was difficult and slow. The oxen that pulled the wagons **plodded** along, covering about ten miles a day, and the people, wearing sturdy shoes and hats with wide brims or bonnets with **visors** to protect them from the sun, walked alongside the wagon.

Every day the pioneers struggled against weather, broken wheels, difficult terrain, injured or dying animals, and poor health. Sometimes wagons were carried down the river or tipped over. Then people tried to **salvage** what they could and often spent the rest of the journey sharing a wagon with another family. Along the way, pioneers hunted for meat and **plucked** berries when they could. They could not always find enough, but the persistent pioneers **shrugged** off their disappointments and went on. At the end of a long day of working and traveling, there might be a little time for **lounging** around the campfire and listening to stories or singing.

Now read the following questions. Then completely fill in the bubble of the correct answer.

1. Which sentence below uses context clues to correctly define *salvage?*
   Ⓐ The pioneers were unable to salvage, or save, any of their belongings after the fire.
   Ⓑ The pioneers were unable to salvage, or make, any of their belongings after the fire.
   Ⓒ The pioneers were unable to salvage, or sell, any of their belongings after the fire.

2. Which word could replace *plucked* in the passage above without changing its meaning?
   Ⓐ chucked
   Ⓑ picked
   Ⓒ replace

3. Which word below is the past tense of *quivering?*
   Ⓐ quivered
   Ⓑ quiveringed
   Ⓒ quiver

4. Which sentence below gives a context clue for *visor?*
   Ⓐ The visor is over there.
   Ⓑ He will protect his eyes by wearing his visor to the game.
   Ⓒ Where is your visor?

# 4 Review Word Meanings

Read the passage below. Then answer the questions about the boldfaced vocabulary words.

## America the Beautiful

After the movement west began, it didn't stop. The United States grew and grew. And what a country it has become! From the protected **dunes** of the Atlantic coast to the **wasteland** of the southwestern states to the sunny California **tidewaters,** there is something for everyone. Museums, zoos, and theaters are among the interesting sites to be found in **urban** areas, such as Cleveland, Miami, Austin, and Seattle. **Suburban** areas offer shopping, parks, schools, churches, and **temples.** In **rural** areas, you can visit farms, nature preserves, lakes, and campgrounds. Perhaps visiting dark **caverns** is to your liking. Maybe you prefer watching wildlife in one of the nation's many **marshes.** Almost any land and practice is available to you in this great country that extends from sea to shining sea.

Now read the following questions. Then completely fill in the bubble of the correct answer.

1. What is the definition of a *dune?*
   A hill or ridge of sand
   B to be finished with something
   C a lemon flavored treat

2. New York City is an example of an _____ area.
   A urban
   B suburban
   C rural

3. Which word below classifies the following?
   *desert, few living things, polar region, barren*
   A marsh
   B cavern
   C wasteland

4. Between which two guide words would you find *rural?*
   A reverse/romance
   B rumor/rush
   C rust/saddle

5. Which of the following words can be written in the past tense?
   A dune
   B marsh
   C plod

6. Which of the following is an antonym for *wasteland?*
   A fertile land
   B desert
   C belt loops

# Cumulative Review

## Definitions

 Write the vocabulary word that matches each definition below. (**Hint:** The vocabulary words may appear in any lesson throughout the book.)

1. made by humans *adj.* _____

2. money owed *n.* _____

3. expecting the worst *adj.* _____

4. supply of food *n.* _____

5. place for water storage *n.* _____

6. flower worn by women *n.* _____

7. to communicate by writing letters *v.* _____

8. to cut apart *v.* _____

9. peaceful *adj.* _____

10. to look at as a whole *v.* _____

11. two-wheeled vehicle pulled by horses *n.*

   _____

12. well-defended place *n.* _____

13. relating to the country *adj.* _____

14. to shake slightly *v.* _____

15. light bluish-green color *adj.* _____

## Synonyms

 Choose the vocabulary word from the box that is a synonym for each word below. Write the vocabulary word in the blank. (**Hint:** Each word is used once.)

| | | | | |
|---|---|---|---|---|
| anxious | dispute | fatal | indifferent | industrious |
| irk | legendary | nauseated | overhaul | passive |
| request | scorch | seldom | suspend | vacant |

1. disagreement _____

2. nervous _____

3. rarely _____

4. famous _____

5. burn _____

6. deadly _____

7. ask _____

8. hard-working _____

9. annoy _____

10. uninterested _____

11. empty _____

12. redo _____

13. hang _____

14. sickened _____

15. inactive _____

## Sentence Completion

 Write the vocabulary word that best completes each sentence below. Each sentence contains a clue related to a lesson theme. (**Hint:** The vocabulary words may appear in any lesson throughout the book.)

1. Wearing a _____ on the beach will help keep the sun out of your eyes.

2. New York, Los Angeles, and Chicago are

   _____ regions of the country because they are large cities.

3. The _____ of an early American settler included a family's house and land.

4. If you're going to meet someone at a restaurant, it is

   important to _____ your watches so that you arrive at the same time.

5. The colors of a piano's keys are _____ and black.

6. A fertile part of Earth that contains water and is normally

   found in a desert is called an _____.

7. The _____ is adjusting to living in the new culture while working as a representative of his country.

8. Emily Post is famous for her tips on good manners; her

   book contains hundreds of rules on _____.

9. The saying, "_____ as a mule" means that you are willful and do not want to follow rules with which you do not agree.

10. The Juilliard School is an _____ where musicians study and perform.

# Words and Themes

Choose two words from the box that belong with each theme below. Write the words in the blank. Try to complete the exercise without looking at the Vocabulary List in each lesson.

1. Vocabulary for Culture _____

2. Vocabulary for Materials _____

3. Risks and Consequences _____

4. "Fashion" Vocabulary _____

5. Dollars and Sense _____

6. Personality Traits _____

7. Dreams to Jobs _____

8. Vocabulary for History _____

9. "Light and Color" Vocabulary

   _____

10. A Changing America _____

11. Earth Words _____

12. "Survival" Vocabulary _____

13. Vocabulary for Debate _____

14. "Communication" Vocabulary _____

15. From Mystery to Medicine

    _____

| currency |
| crusade |
| instinct |
| stern |
| adobe |
| civilization |
| crinoline |
| venture |
| gorge |
| prevail |
| microscopic |
| internship |
| variation |
| inexpensive |
| irk |
| document |
| heritage |
| plateau |
| crimson |
| reply |
| declaration |
| stylish |
| granite |
| conviction |
| cautious |
| equipment |
| industrious |
| recuperate |
| generous |
| inform |

# Word Maps

You can draw a **word map** to help you understand what a word means and remember how to use it in a sentence, or context. The word maps below are for vocabulary words in this book.

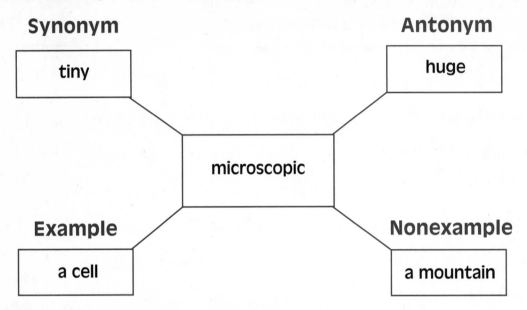

**Vocabulary Word Used in an Example Sentence:** *Cells are microscopic.*

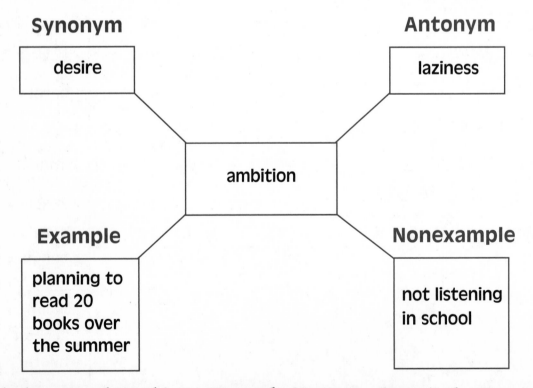

**Vocabulary Word Used in an Example Sentence:** *Logan's plan to read 20 books this summer shows that he has ambition.*

# Categorization

A **category** is a kind of group. By placing words into categories, you can better remember their meanings. Categorization is a strategy that can help you learn new words in any subject.

## Vocabulary Words Before Categorization

| | | |
|---|---|---|
| recuperate | ambassador | bandage |
| employ | cure | designer |
| ivory | crimson | violet |
| treatment | geologist | infection |
| teal | professional | indigo |

## Vocabulary Words After Categorization

### Career Words

designer

ambassador

employ

geologist

professional

### Colors

indigo

crimson

ivory

teal

violet

### Medical Words

recuperate

cure

treatment

bandage

infection

# Linear Graphs

**A linear graph** shows how words relate to each other.

Some linear graphs show degree. The example below can help you remember that *wonderful* is better than *good* and *dreadful* is worse than *bad*.

wonderful ➡ good ➡ bad ➡ dreadful

The linear graph below shows size.

large ➡ medium ➡ small ➡ microscopic

You can also use a linear graph to show progression, or development. The example graph below shows how an infection leads to a treatment, which results in a cure. Finally the patient gets well again, or recuperates.

infection ➡ treatment ➡ cure ➡ recuperate

A linear graph can also help you picture what words mean.

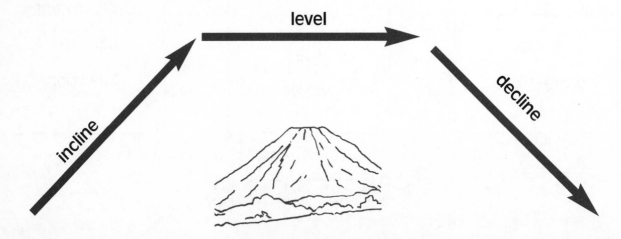

# Context Clues

You will learn many new words from reading. **Context clues** are words, phrases, and sentences that tell something about an unknown word. Sometimes context clues clearly tell a word's meaning, but other times they only hint at it.

## Steps for Using Context Clues

1. Find the unknown word.
2. List the words or phrases that tell something about its meaning.
3. Reread the sentence that contains the unknown word, and list clues found in that sentence. If you need more clues, reread the sentences before and after the one that contains the unknown word, and list those clues.
4. Guess the meaning of the unknown word based on your list of clues.

The following is a list of some types of context clues.

## Definition Context Clues

The definition, or meaning, of the unknown word might be in the sentence or a nearby sentence.

> **Our concert will be in an *auditorium*, which is a large room used for public gatherings.**

The word *auditorium* is defined in the sentence as "a large room used for public gatherings."

**Clue Words:** *or, in other words, that is, which is, which means*

## Example Context Clues

There might be examples of the unknown word in the sentence or nearby sentences.

> **In the nature room we saw many different *minerals*, such as petroleum, gold, copper, and coal.**

*Petroleum, gold, copper,* and *coal* are examples of *minerals.*

**Clue Words:** *for example, for instance, including, such as*

# Context Clues

## Cause-and-Effect Context Clues

The unknown word might be explained as a part of a cause-and-effect relationship.

**Because the *deadline* is tomorrow, I worked all day on my paper.**

The *deadline* is the cause, and *working all day on my paper* is the effect. You can tell from the sentence that a *deadline* is a time limit.

**Clue Words:** *as a result, because, consequently, therefore, thus*

## Comparison Context Clues

The unknown word might be compared to a word or phrase that has the same meaning. To compare is to find similarities between things.

**John was *ecstatic* about the new song. Ringo was also overjoyed.**

*Ecstatic* and *overjoyed* have the same meaning. They are synonyms. In the sentences above, John and Ringo feel the same way.

**Clue Words:** *also, same, resembling, identical, similarly, too, likewise, like*

## Contrast Context Clues

The unknown word might be contrasted with another word or phrase. To contrast is to find differences between things.

**Many doctors examine patients, but *surgeons* are licensed to operate on them.**

The sentence tells you that *surgeons* are different from the average doctor— they are doctors who can operate on patients.

**Clue Words:** *however, but, on the other hand, on the contrary, unlike*

# Word Relationships

## Synonyms

A **synonym** is a word or a phrase that means the same or nearly the same as another word. The words *vacant* and *empty* are synonyms.

> **The front room was *vacant*.**
> **The front room was *empty*.**

The sentences above mean the same thing.

Sometimes synonyms do not have *exactly* the same meanings. For example, the word *hot* is different from the word *warm*.

## Antonyms

An **antonym** is a word that has the opposite meaning of another word. For example, the words *cautious* and *daring* are antonyms.

> **The child was *cautious* when he played with his new toys.**
> **The child was *daring* when he played with his new toys.**

Changing the word *cautious* to its antonym *daring* changes the meaning of the sentence.

## Homographs

**Homographs** are words that are spelled the same but have different meanings. Sometimes homographs are pronounced differently.

> **He turned *left* as he *left* our house.**

    direction        moved away from

## Homophones

**Homophones** are words that sound the same but have different meanings and are usually spelled differently.

> **I can see the *whole* city through that *hole* in the wall.**

entire amount         an opening

# Word Relationships

## Analogies

An **analogy** shows how two pairs of words are related. To complete an analogy, look at the first pair of words and decide how they relate to each other. The second pair of words relates in the same way, so you need to choose a word that shows the same relationship.

The boxes below show some common types of analogies with examples.

---

### Synonym Analogies

The words in each pair are synonyms.

*minimum* is to *least* as *maximum* is to *most*

*pluck* is to *pick* as *suspend* is to *hang*

---

### Antonym Analogies

The words in each pair are antonyms.

*gloomy* is to *cheerful* as *exit* is to *entrance*

*brilliant* is to *dull* as *scorch* is to *freeze*

---

### Part-to-Whole Analogies

The first word in each pair is part of the second word.

*shirt* is to *wardrobe* as *toe* is to *foot*

*page* is to *book* as *yolk* is to *egg*

---

### Object-to-Use Analogies

The first word in each pair is an object, and the second word tells what you do with it.

*food* is to *eat* as *book* is to *read*

*car* is to *drive* as *pencil* is to *write*

---

# Building Vocabulary Skills

## Level 4

# Notebook Reference

To Reinforce Vocabulary Skills

## Tools and Reference

### Table of Contents

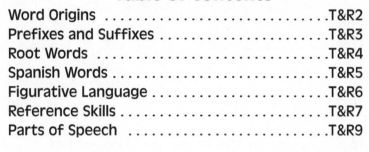

## www.sra4kids.com

Send all inquiries to:
SRA/McGraw-Hill
8787 Orion Place
Columbus, OH 43240-4027

Printed in the United States of America.

R00004412

2 3 4 5 6 7 8 9 QPD 07 06 05 04 03

*Columbus, OH • Chicago, IL • Redmond, WA*

The McGraw·Hill Companies

# Word Origins

*Origin* means "beginning" or "source." The origin of a word is where and when the word was first used. Many English words come from words that were first used in ancient Rome, where people spoke Latin. English words also come from other languages, such as Greek, French, German, and Spanish.

A dictionary entry might include the origin of the entry word. It may also list the date when the word was first used in the English language. An entry that includes the origin of a word will look like this:

> **au di tor i um** /ô′ di tôr′ ē əm/ *n. pl* **–riums** or **–ria** [*Latin,* from *audire, to hear*] (1751) **1:** the part of a public building where an audience sits **2:** a room, hall, or building used for public gatherings

The dictionary entry above tells you that *auditorium* was first used in the English language in 1751 and came from a Latin word that meant "to hear."

The next dictionary entry includes the origin of the word *violet.*

> **vi o let** /vī′ ə lət/ *n.* [*French,* from *violete, Latin,* from *viola*] (14c) **1:** a small, purple, white, or rose-colored flower of a plant found in Europe, Africa, and Asia **2:** a bluish purple color.

This dictionary entry tells you that *violet* came from two languages—first Latin, then French. It also tells you that *violet* was first used in English in the 1300s (the fourteenth century).

# Prefixes and Suffixes

**Prefixes** can be added to the beginning of base words or root words to make new words.

| Prefix | Meaning | Examples |
|---|---|---|
| *auto-* | self | autobiography, automobile |
| *dis-* | not; opposite | dishonest, disagree |
| *im-, in-* | not | impossible, insecure |
| *micro-* | small; short | microscopic, microwave |
| *mis-* | wrong; not | misbehave, misuse |
| *mono-* | one | monogram, monorail |
| *non-* | not | nonstop, nonsense |
| *pre-* | before | preheat, precaution |
| *re-* | back | redo, recharge |
| *un-* | not | unspeakable, uncertain |
| *sub-* | under | submarine, subdivision |

**Suffixes** can be added to the end of base words or root words to make new words.

| Suffix | Meaning | Examples |
|---|---|---|
| *-able, -ible* | is; can be | bearable, comfortable |
| *-ance, -ence* | state or quality of | abundance, consequence |
| *-er, -or* | one who | explorer, driver |
| *-est* | most | highest, largest |
| *-ful* | full of | fearful, meaningful |
| *-an, -ian* | relating to | American, comedian |
| *-ist* | one who practices | specialist, biologist |
| *-ous* | full of | joyous, nervous |
| *-ty* | state or quality of | honesty, unity |
| *-ive* | inclined to | active, passive |

# Root Words

A **root word** is the basic part of a word that gives the word its meaning. Some root words are called *base words.* You can add a prefix, suffix, or both to a root word. If you do not know what a word means, look for its root.

| Root Word | Word Forms |
|---|---|
| *teach* | teacher, teaching, reteach, teachable, reteaching |
| *active* | inactive, activity, reactive |
| *view* | preview, viewer, viewed, review |

## Greek and Latin Roots

Some root words come from the Greek and Latin languages. Many Greek and Latin roots cannot stand alone as words in English. Like all root words, though, Greek and Latin roots having a meaning.

### Greek Roots

| Root | Meaning | Words |
|---|---|---|
| *bio* | life | biology, biography |
| *cycl* | circle; ring | bicycle, recycle |
| *hydr* | water | hydrogen, dehydrate |
| *photo* | light | photograph, photosynthesis |
| *poli* | city | police, metropolis |
| *therm* | heat | thermometer, thermal |

### Latin Roots

| Root | Meaning | Words |
|---|---|---|
| *aqua* | water | aquarium, aquamarine |
| *doc* | teach | document, doctor |
| *form* | shape | uniform, formal |
| *ject* | throw | project, eject |
| *min* | small; less | minimum, minor |
| *ped* | foot | pedal, pedestrian |
| *sect* | cut | intersect, dissect |
| *sign* | mark | signature, signal |
| *vac* | empty | vacant, evacuate |
| *volv* | turn | revolution, involve |

# Spanish Words

The English language contains many words that are borrowed from Spanish. The list below shows some of these words. The Spanish words used in English may be changed from their original spellings in Spanish.

## Spanish Words

| | |
|---|---|
| **adios** | good-bye |
| **adobe** | sun-baked brick made of earth |
| **albino** | lack of normal coloring |
| **alfalfa** | a plant resembling clover |
| **avocado** | a tropical fruit |
| **armada** | a large fleet of warships |
| **bronco** | an untamed horse |
| **cafeteria** | a room used for eating |
| **canoe** | a boat |
| **canyon** | a deep valley |
| **chocolate** | food made from cacao beans |
| **corral** | an enclosure for cattle |
| **fiesta** | a party |
| **hurricane** | a very windy rainstorm |
| **mesa** | flat-topped hill |
| **Montana** | western U.S. state |
| **mosquito** | an insect |
| **patio** | a paved outdoor area |
| **plaza** | a public square |
| **poncho** | an outer garment |
| **potato** | a vegetable |
| **ranch** | a large farm |
| **tomato** | a fruit plant |
| **tornado** | a wind funnel |
| **tortilla** | a thin, round cake made of cornmeal |

# Figurative Language

**Figurative language** is the use of words in a creative way to mean something different from the usual meanings of words. Common types of figurative language are shown below.

---

## Similes

A **simile** compares two things that are not the same by using the words *like* or *as.*

>**Example:** *This bread is as hard as a rock.*

The sentence compares the bread to a rock to describe how hard it is.

---

## Metaphors

A **metaphor** compares two things that are not the same without using the words *like* or *as.*

>**Example:** *Stars are bright diamonds shining in the night sky.*

The sentence compares stars to diamonds that sparkle brightly.

---

## Hyperbole, or Exaggeration

A **hyperbole** is an exaggeration used to make a point.

>**Example:** *My hand fell off after I wrote that report.*

Did the person's hand really fall off? No. This hyperbole just tells you that his or her hand was tired from writing a lot.

---

## Idioms

An **idiom** is an expression that cannot be understood from the words themselves.

>**Example:** *I need to hit the books.*

This idiom means "I need to study." It does not *really* mean "I am going to punch the books."

# Reference Skills

## The Parts of a Dictionary Entry

Study the parts of a dictionary entry below. Some dictionary entries may not include *all* of the information shown in the sample entry.

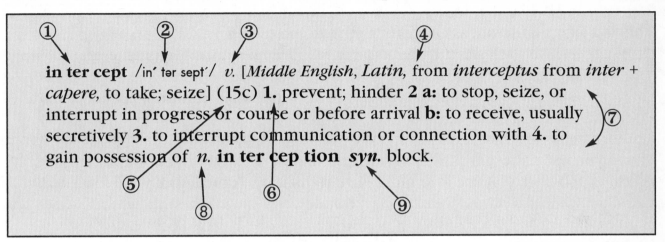

1. **Entry Word with Syllabication** – shows how to spell the word and how many syllables the word has
2. **Phonetic Spelling** – shows how to say the word
3. **Part of Speech** – shows the part of speech, which tells you how to use the word in a sentence
4. **Word Origin** – tells where the word was first used
5. **Date of First Use in English** – tells when the word was first used in the English language (*c* means "century")
6. **Most Common Definition** – gives the definition that is used most often in English
7. **Other Definitions** – gives other definitions, or multiple meanings, for the word
8. **Other Forms** –shows other forms of the word
9. **Synonym** – gives one or more synonyms for the word

# Reference Skills

## Thesaurus

A **thesaurus** includes a list of synonyms and antonyms for each entry word. A thesaurus is a handy writing tool because it helps you find new words for words you have already used.

This is a sample thesaurus entry for the word *delighted:*

> **delighted** *adj. My little sister was delighted when she received a new doll for her birthday:* pleased, captivated, enthralled, enchanted, elated, ecstatic. *Ant.* displeased, disgusted

When you use a thesaurus, it is important to look up a synonym or antonym in a dictionary before you use it to make sure it fits in the context of your sentence.

## Encyclopedia

An **encyclopedia** includes articles on many different topics. These articles are listed in alphabetical order. An encyclopedia provides more information than a dictionary entry. Most encyclopedias are printed in many volumes, and most have an index to help you locate your information quickly.

## Rhyming Dictionary

A **rhyming dictionary** lists words that rhyme. If you are writing a song or a poem and need a word that rhymes, this is the place to look. Many rhyming dictionaries are also available on the Internet.

## Internet Search Engine

Using the **Internet** as a research tool can help you find a lot of information very quickly. Be sure to spell your keyword correctly in the search engine box in order to get the best choices. Sometimes you will have to search a few different Web sites before finding the information you need.

# Parts of Speech

## Nouns

**Nouns** name everything. For example, nouns name persons, places, things (this includes animals), and ideas. *Rachel, girl, apartment, hamster,* and *freedom* are all nouns.

## Pronouns

**Pronouns** can take the place of a noun or nouns, so you do not have to keep repeating the same word when you are writing.

> **Without Pronouns:** *Sandra* left *Sandra's* bag in *Sandra* and *Michael's* mother's car this morning.
>
> **With Pronouns:** Sandra left *her* bag in *their* mother's car this morning.

The pronouns *her* and *their* replace the overused nouns in the sentence.

## Verbs

**Verbs** show action, state of being, or ownership. *Wiggle* is a verb because it is an action. *Is* is a verb because it shows state of being. *Has* shows ownership.

## Adjectives

**Adjectives** are words used to describe nouns or pronouns. Adjectives usually answer one of these questions: *What kind? Which one? How much or how many?*

> **Leroy likes *jazz* music.**

*Jazz* is the adjective describing the noun *music*. It tells the kind of music Leroy likes.

## Adverbs

**Adverbs** are words that describe verbs, adjectives, or other adverbs. Adverbs usually answer one of these questions: *When? Where? How? Why? Under what conditions? To what extreme?*

> **Mariah runs *fast*.**

*Fast* is the adverb describing the verb *runs*. It tells how Mariah runs.

## Conjunctions

**Conjunctions** connect words or groups of words to each other.

> **They wanted to go to the movies, *but* they did not have any money.**
>
> **I forgot my speech *because* I was nervous.**

*But* and *because* are conjunctions that connect two sentences to make one sentence in each example.

# Glossary

**A**

**a bol ish** /ə bol′ ish/ *v.* **abolishes, abolishing, abolished.** to put an end to. *A law abolishes the use of cell phones in cars.*

**a brupt ly** /ə brupt′ lē/ *adv.* **1.** suddenly; unexpectedly. *The taxicab stopped abruptly at the stop sign.* **2.** bluntly; impolitely. *My uncle speaks very abruptly on the telephone.*

**a bun dance** /ə bun′ dəns/ *n.* a large amount; an amount that is more than enough. *There was an abundance of books at the library sale.*

**a cad e my** /ə kad′ ə mē/ *n., pl.* **academies.** a school that trains people in a special field. *She attends a music academy there.*

**ac ces so ries** /ak ses′ ə rēz/ *n. pl.* **1.** pieces added to clothing for looks. *Belts and scarves are accessories for women's dresses.* **2.** items added to a more important thing. *Special wheel covers are automobile accessories.*

**ad mis sion** /ad mish′ ən/ *n.* the payment needed to enter. *Admission to the theater was five dollars.*

**a do be** /ə dō′ bē/ *n.* **1.** sun-dried clay brick. *Adobe is sometimes mixed with straw and dried in the sun.* **2.** a building made of such bricks. *You can find adobes in the American Southwest.*

**af fec tion ate** /ə fek′ shə nit/ *adj.* loving; full of love. *My grandfather is very affectionate with children.*

**a lu mi num** /ə lōō′ mə nəm/ *n.* a silver metal. *Aluminum is used in making machines, airplanes, and pots and pans.*

**am bas sa dor** /am bas′ ə dər/ *n.* a representative of a country. *Ambassadors represent their own countries while living abroad.*

**am bi tion** /am bish′ ən/ *n.* **1.** a strong desire to achieve. *She shows little ambition in ballet class.* **2.** the object of such a desire. *My ambition is to become an astronaut.*

**anx ious** /angk′ shəs/ *adj.* worried or fearful about something. *The family was anxious when they heard of the approaching hurricane.*

**ap palled** /ə pôld′/ *v.* a form of **appall.** to fill with horror or shock. *The damage done by the terrible flood appalled the comminity.*

**ap pre ci a tion** /ə prē′ shē ā′ shən/ *n.* thankfulness; gratitude. *I wrote my uncle a note in appreciation for his help with my tennis game.*

**aq ua** /äk′ wə/ *n.* a light bluish-green color. *I chose aqua for my bedroom walls.*

**as pi ra tion** /as′ pə rā′ shən/ *n.* a high goal. *My aspiration is to become a doctor.*

**as set** /as′ et/ *n.* a thing that has cash value. *They said that our home security system will protect our assets.*

**au di to ri um** /ô′ di tor′ ē əm/ *n., pl.* **auditoriums.** a large public meeting room. *The candidates' debate will be held in the auditorium this spring.*

**B**

**bal co ny** /bal′ kə nē/ *n., pl.* **balconies.** **1.** the upper floor of an auditorium. *Our seats in the balcony allowed us to see all the action on the stage.*

**2.** a platform that extends from the outside of a building. *She keeps tomato plants and a chair on her sunny balcony.*

**band age** /ban′ dij/ *n.* a strip of material that covers a wound. *A bandage covered the scrape on my knee.* *v.* **bandages, bandaging, bandaged.** to cover with a bandage. *The nurse bandaged his cut.*

**bar gain** /bär′ gin/ *n.*
**1.** something sold at a low price. *This doll is a bargain at thirty dollars.* **2.** an agreement or deal. *I made a bargain with my brother to help him with his homework.* *v.* **bargains, bargaining, bargained.** to talk over the terms of an agreement. *I bargained for ten minutes with the street merchant.*

**ba zaar** /bə zär′/ *n.*
a marketplace. *The bazaar was full of stalls selling food, rugs, and other goods.*

**bond** /bond/ *n.* something that binds, fastens, or holds together. *Even though we live far apart, our friendship is the bond that connects us.*

**bon go** /bong′ gō/ *n., pl.* **bongos.** a small drum played with the hands and held between the knees. *She played the bongos while I danced.*

**bril liant** /bril′ yənt/ *adj.* shining brightly. *The brilliant lights of fireworks can be seen for miles.*

*C*

**can vas** /kan′ vəs/ *n., pl.* **canvases.** a strong, heavy cloth. *Canvas is used for tents, backpacks, and sails.*

**ca pa ble** /kā′ pə bəl/ *adj.* being able; having skill or power. *A capable tailor can fix any garment.*

**cap size** /kap′ sīz/ *v.* **capsizes, capsizing, capsized.** to turn upside down. *Strong winds or rough waves can capsize a small boat.*

**cau tious** /kô′ shəs/ *adj.* careful; watchful. *She is cautious when crossing a busy street.*

**cav ern** /kav′ ərn/ *n.* an underground cave. *Caverns are large caves created by water moving underground.*

**cel e brat ed** /sel′ ə brā′ tid/ *adj.* a form of **celebrate.** famous. *The celebrated opera singer received three curtain calls after his performance.*

**chal lenge** /chal′ ənj/ *n.* difficult situation. *Lewis and Clark faced many challenges when they traveled west.* *v.* **challenges, challenged, challenging.** **1.** to dare or invite to a contest. *He challenged the stranger to a race to the end of the block.* **2.** to question or doubt. *Do you challenge my statement?*

**char i ot** /char′ ē ət/ *n.* a two-wheeled vehicle pulled by horses. *Chariots were used in ancient times for races and processions.*

| | |
|---|---|
| /a/ | at |
| /ā/ | late |
| /â/ | care |
| /ä/ | father |
| /e/ | set |
| /ē/ | me |
| /i/ | it |
| /ī/ | kite |
| /o/ | ox |
| /ō/ | rose |
| /ô/ | brought |
| | raw |
| /oi/ | coin |
| /o͝o/ | book |
| /o͞o/ | too |
| /or/ | form |
| /ou/ | out |
| /u/ | up |
| /yo͞o/ | cube |
| /ûr/ | turn |
| | germ |
| | learn |
| | firm |
| | work |
| /ə/ | about |
| | chicken |
| | pencil |
| | cannon |
| | circus |
| /ch/ | chair |
| /hw/ | which |
| /ng/ | ring |
| /sh/ | shop |
| /th/ | thin |
| /ŧħ/ | there |
| /zh/ | treasure |

**char i ty** /chȧr′ i tē/ *n., pl.* **charities.**
**1.** an organization that helps the poor or people in need. *We give money to this charity once a year.* **2.** the giving of money or help to people in need. *His charity was greatly appreciated.*

**charm ing** /chär′ ming/ *adj.* a form of **charm.** enjoyable; attractive; full of charm. *The garden surrounded my grandparents' charming old house.*

**civ i li za tion** /siv′ ə lə zā′ shən/ *n.*
**1.** the way of life of a particular people, place, or time. *In the tenth century, Mayan civilization included more than 40 cities with thousands of people in each one.* **2.** the condition of human society in which science, trade, art, government, and agriculture are highly developed. *The growth of communities and the use of writing mark the beginning of civilization.*

**clas sic** /klas′ ik/ *adj.* of high quality. *Gulliver's Travels is a classic children's story.*

**com mu ni ty** /kə myoo′ ni tē/ *n., pl.* **communities. 1.** a group of people who live together in the same place. *We are a friendly community of students at our school.* **2.** the area or place itself. *That community is west of Chicago.*

**com pe ti tion** /kom′ pi tish′ ən/ *n.* **1.** the act of competing; rivalry. *The competition to get into that school is great.* **2.** something that tests or proves skill or ability; contest. *Keep your poise and you will win the theater competition.*

**com ple tion** /kəm plē′ shən/ *n.* the act of finishing. *At the completion of my project, I had time for other things.*

**con di tion** /kən dish′ ən/ *n.* **1.** a disease or ailment. *Chronic health conditions worsen in winter.* **2.** the way a person or thing is. *An athlete stays in good condition through regular exercise and training.* *v.* **conditions, conditioning, conditioned.** to put in a healthful condition. *Exercise conditions the muscles.*

**con front** /kən frunt′/ *v.* **confronts, confronting, confronted.** to meet or to face. *The twins confront the problem of being accepted by different colleges.*

**con science** /kon′ shəns/ *n.* the sense of understanding right and wrong. *When pressured by others, choose by listening to your conscience.*

**con se quence** /kon′ si kwens′/ *n.* **1.** the result of an action. *A consequence of going to sleep late is feeling tired the next morning.* **2.** importance; significance. *Reports in the gossip columns are of no consequence to me.*

**con sid er ate** /kən sid′ ər it/ *adj.* caring about others; having or showing respect for others and their feelings. *Our considerate neighbors watered our plants while we vacationed.*

**con tent** /kən tent′/ *adj.* wanting nothing else. *The cat is content to sleep on the sofa all day.*

**con ven ience** /kən vēn′ yəns/ *n.* **1.** ease and comfort. *We like the convenience of using precut and prepackaged vegetables.* **2.** a useful thing. *The dishwasher is a modern convenience.*

**con vic tion** /kən vik′ shən/ *n.* **1.** a strong belief. *My conviction is that everyone deserves to be heard.* **2.** the state of being found guilty of a crime. *The conviction put the criminal in prison for ten years.*

**cor re spond** /kôr´ ə spond´/ *v.* **corresponds, corresponding, corresponded.** to communicate by writing letters. *I correspond with a pen pal in France.*

**cor sage** /kôr säzh´/ *n.* a flower or small bunch of flowers usually worn by a woman. *My older sister wore a corsage of orchids on her wrist.*

**crest** /krest/ *n.* highest point or part of something. *Surfers like to ride the crest of a wave.*

**crim son** /krim´ zən/ *n.* a deep red color. *Crimson and white are our school colors.*

**crin o line** /krin´ ə lin/ *n.* a stiff skirt lining. *Before the Civil War, women in the South wore dresses with crinolines underneath.*

**crouch** /krouch/ *v.* **crouches, crouching, crouched.** to bend low; to stoop with the knees bent. *Cats crouch before they leap or jump.*

**cru sade** /kroō sād´/ *n.* movement against something seen as evil or for a cause. *The city council called for a more active crusade against crime.*

**cure** /kyoŏr/ *v.* **cures, curing, cured.** to make well again. *An aspirin cured my headache. n.* something that makes a person or an animal well again. *Many doctors work on finding cures for diseases.*

**cur ren cy** /kûr´ ən sē/ *n., pl.* **currencies.** the money used in a country. *The yen is the currency used in Japan.*

**D**

**dar ing** /dâr´ ing/ *adj.* a form of **dare.** fearless; brave. *The stuntman performed a daring jump.*

**day dream** /dā´ drēm´/ *n.* dreamy imagining; a pleasant thought about things one would like to have happen. *I have a daydream about being a famous musician.*

**dead line** /ded´ lin´/ *n.* a time set for the completion of something. *The deadline for finishing the science project is next Thursday.*

**debt** /det/ *n.* money owed. *Pay your debts before buying luxuries.*

**dec la ra tion** /dek´ lə rā´ shən/ *n.* a formal statement; the act of making something known. *The Declaration of Independence was made on July 4, 1776.*

**de cline** /di klin´/ *n.* a lessening or weakening; increasingly poor condition. *The decline of the Roman Empire began in the third century. v.* **declines, declining, declined.** to refuse politely. *We declined the invitation to go to the play on Friday.*

**ded i cat ed** /ded´ i kā´ təd/ *adj.* a form of **dedicate.** totally committed to a cause or a purpose. *Florence Nightingale was dedicated to the profession of nursing.*

**de light ed** /di li´ tid/ *adj.* a form of **delight.** pleased. *My mother was delighted when I cleaned my room.*

| | |
|---|---|
| /a/ | at |
| /ā/ | late |
| /â/ | care |
| /ä/ | father |
| /e/ | set |
| /ē/ | me |
| /i/ | it |
| /ī/ | kite |
| /o/ | ox |
| /ō/ | rose |
| /ô/ | brought raw |
| /oi/ | coin |
| /oŏ/ | book |
| /oō/ | too |
| /or/ | form |
| /ou/ | out |
| /u/ | up |
| /yoō/ | cube |
| /ûr/ | turn germ learn firm work |
| /ə/ | about chicken pencil cannon circus |
| /ch/ | chair |
| /hw/ | which |
| /ng/ | ring |
| /sh/ | shop |
| /th/ | thin |
| /ŧh/ | there |
| /zh/ | treasure |

**de mand ing** /di man′ ding/ *adj.* a form of **demand.** needing much attention. *Being a police officer is a very demanding job.*

**de sign er** /di zī′ nər/ *n.* a person who creates styles or patterns for clothing or other goods. *Automobile designers create new models several years in advance of their production.*

**de spise** /di spīz′/ *v.* **despises, despising, despised.** to hate; to look down upon as worthless. *My father despises lying of any kind.*

**des ti na tion** /des′ tə nā′ shən/ *n.* a place to which someone or something is going. *My destination is Dallas.*

**de vel op** /di vel′ əp/ *v.* **develops, developing, developed. 1.** to grow or cause to grow. *You can develop your juggling skills by practicing.* **2.** to come into being. *I developed an interest in horses at the age of six.*

**dig ni tar y** /dig′ ni ter′ ē/ *n., pl.* **dignitaries.** a government official. *The dignitaries gathered for a conference on world trade.*

**dis pute** /di spyo͞ot′/ *v.* **disputes, disputing, disputed.** to argue against or disagree with. *The guest disputed every statement made by the talk show host. n.* an argument or quarrel. *The neighbors' dispute went on for a week.*

**dis sect** /di sekt′/ *v.* **dissects, dissecting, dissected.** to cut apart for study or scientific examination. *Scientists dissect animals to learn about organs.*

**doc u ment** /dok′ yə mənt/ *n.* a written or printed statement that gives official information. *A birth certificate is a document that tells the place and date of a person's birth.*

**dra mat ic** /drə mat′ ik/ *adj.* exciting or striking in quality or effect. *By scoring a goal in the last minute, the soccer team won a dramatic victory.*

**dread ful** /dred′ fəl/ *adj.* **1.** causing fear or awe; terrible. *The dreadful creature was finally captured at the end of the movie.* **2.** awful; very bad. *In my opinion, the movie was dreadful.*

**dune** /do͞on/ *n.* a hill or ridge of sand. *Dunes slowly change shape as winds blow the sand around.*

**dy nas ty** /dī′ nə stē/ *n., pl.* **dynasties.** a line of rulers from one family. *The Ming dynasty ruled China for more than 250 years.*

## E

**earn** /ûrn/ *v.* **earns, earning, earned. 1.** to get in return for work. *My friend earned fifty dollars as a baby-sitter.* **2.** to deserve or obtain as a reward. *I studied hard and earned high marks on the final exam.*

**ebb** /eb/ *n.* **1.** the flowing of the ocean away from the shore. *At the tide's ebb, we could walk a long way on the sand to the water.* **2.** a point of decline. *After one year in the limelight, his popularity was at a low ebb.*

**e con o my** /i kon′ ə mē/ *n., pl.* **economies.** a system of managing the use of money, goods, and services. *We studied the Russian economy in history class.*

**ec stat ic** /ek stat′ ik/ *adj.* overwhelmed with joy or delight. *The students were ecstatic about the field trip to the space camp.*

**edg y** /ej′ ē/ *adj.* impatient or nervous. *Speaking in front of the class makes me edgy.*

**el e gant** /el′ i gənt/ *adj.* showing grace. *The elegant dancers waltzed effortlessly across the ballroom.*

**em ploy** /em ploi′/ *v.* **employs, employing, employed. 1.** to give a job to; to hire. *Several neighbors employ my brother as a gardener each summer.* **2.** to use. *He employs rakes, hoes, spades, and shears in his gardening work.*

**e nam el** /i nam′ əl/ *n.* a hard, glossy coating. *Enamel is used to decorate and protect pottery.*

**en dure** /en do͝or′/ *v.* **endures, enduring, endured. 1.** to put up with; to undergo and survive. *The lost animal was able to endure the harsh climate and the threat of attack.* **2.** to continue or last. *Our friendship will endure forever.*

**en raged** /en rājd′/ *v.* a form of **enrage.** to make angry. *The matador's red cape enraged the bull.*

**en thu si as tic** /en tho͞o′ zē as′ tik/ *adj.* full of energy; interested and excited about something. *Our family is enthusiastic about camping in the woods.*

**en vy** /en′ vē/ *v.* **envies, envying, envied.** to want what another has. *I envied her ability to play soccer. n.* an object of notice or feeling. *My new tennis racket made me the envy of my friends.*

**e quip ment** /i kwip′ mənt/ *n.* supplies; anything provided for a particular use or purpose. *Our ski equipment took up a lot of room in the car.*

**es tab lish** /e stab′ lish/ *v.* **establishes, establishing, established. 1.** to set up; to begin or create. *The college established a new scholarship for students.* **2.** to show or prove to be true. *Police established that he was far from the crime scene.*

**es teem** /e stēm′/ *v.* **esteems, esteeming, esteemed.** to consider good; to respect. *The students esteemed their teacher for his hard work in rebuilding the school. n.* respect or regard. *Your devotion to our school earned you the esteem of all.*

**et i quette** /et′ i kit/ *n.* rules for good behavior. *Proper etiquette and good manners go hand in hand.*

**e vac u ate** /i vak′ yo͞o āt′/ *v.* **evacuates, evacuating, evacuated.** to leave or cause to leave; to empty out. *Many people evacuated their homes when the forest fire spread.*

**ex ag ger a tion** /eg zaj′ ə rā′ shən/ *n.* something that appears greater or more important than it is. *Their story about petting wild animals in South America was an exaggeration.*

| | |
|---|---|
| /a/ | at |
| /ā/ | late |
| /â/ | care |
| /ä/ | father |
| /e/ | set |
| /ē/ | me |
| /i/ | it |
| /ī/ | kite |
| /o/ | ox |
| /ō/ | rose |
| /ô/ | brought |
| | raw |
| /oi/ | coin |
| /o͝o/ | book |
| /o͞o/ | too |
| /or/ | form |
| /ou/ | out |
| /u/ | up |
| /yo͞o/ | cube |
| /ûr/ | turn |
| | germ |
| | learn |
| | firm |
| | work |
| /ə/ | about |
| | chicken |
| | pencil |
| | cannon |
| | circus |
| /ch/ | chair |
| /hw/ | which |
| /ng/ | ring |
| /sh/ | shop |
| /th/ | thin |
| /t͟h/ | there |
| /zh/ | treasure |

**ex empt** /eg zempt´/ *v.* to free from or excuse. *We were exempted from the test because we chose to do the project.*

**ex pec ta tions** /ek´ spek tā´ shənz/ *n. pl.* reasons for hoping. *After studying all week, I have high expectations of a good grade on this English test.*

**ex posed** /ek spōzd´/ *v.* a form of **expose. 1.** to uncover or reveal. *The newspaper exposed the company's financial problems.* **2.** to leave open or without protection. *I was exposed to the measles when my sister had them.*

**F** ▬▬▬▬▬▬▬▬▬▬▬▬▬▬

**fan tas tic** /fan tas´ tic/ *adj.* **1.** very strange or unusual. *Wind and water shaped these fantastic landforms.* **2.** very good; excellent. *The magicians put on a fantastic performance tonight.*

**fa tal** /fā´ təl/ *adj.* resulting in death. *Prevent fatal accidents by decreasing your car's speed.*

**fire** /fīr/ *v.* **fires, firing, fired. 1.** to dismiss from a job. *To save money, the company fired 200 workers.* **2.** to spark; to cause to be stirred up. *Stories about knights in shining armor have always fired my imagination. n.* the flame, heat, and light given off when some substances burn. *The fire warmed us.*

**flash** /flash/ *n.* a quick burst of light. *The flash of lightning sent us all indoors. v.* to burst out in sudden light or fire. *Lightning flashed in the dark sky.*

**for bid den** /fər bi´ dən/ *adj.* a form of **forbid.** not allowed. *Eating in most retail stores is forbidden.*

**for tress** /for´ tris/ *n., pl.* **fortresses.** a well-defended place; a fort. *The Russian government has its central offices in an old fortress that dates from 1156.*

**fre quent** /frē´ kwənt/ *adj.* happening often; regular. *During the long drive, I take frequent breaks to stretch and eat.*

**fric tion** /frik´ shən/ *n.* **1.** the rubbing of one object against another. *The friction of the rope on my hands hurt as I slid to the gym floor.* **2.** a force that resists movement between two touching surfaces. *Oil is used to reduce the friction between the parts of a machine.*

**G** ▬▬▬▬▬▬▬▬▬▬▬▬▬▬

**gal ax y** /gal´ ək sē/ *n., pl.* **galaxies.** a very large grouping of stars. *The sun is one of billions of stars in the Milky Way galaxy.*

**gal ler y** /gal´ ə rē/ *n., pl.* **galleries.** a place where works of art are sold or shown. *The art gallery had sculptures by a local artist on exhibit.*

**gen er ous** /jen´ ər əs/ *adj.* **1.** willing to share; not selfish. *Generous people often give money to charity.* **2.** plentiful; large. *The cafe served such generous portions that we took home the remaining food.*

**ge ol o gist** /jē ol´ ə jist/ *n.* a scientist who studies Earth's surface. *Geologists study rocks to find out what changes Earth has undergone over the years.*

**ghet to** /get´ ō/ *n., pl.* **ghettos** or **ghettoes.** a separated area of town. *Many families were forced to live in the ghettos.*

**gid dy** /gid′ ē/ *adj.* **1.** silly. *The giddy children laughed as they watched cartoons.* **2.** dizzy. *I'm always a bit giddy after a ride on a roller coaster.*

**gi gan tic** /jī gan′ tik/ *adj.* huge; enormous. *The top of the gigantic mountain was covered with snow.*

**glen** /glen/ *n.* a small, narrow valley. *A glen in the forest provided a quiet place to rest.*

**gloom y** /gloo′ mē/ *adj.* **1.** sad. *Losing the game made us gloomy.* **2.** dim. *In the gloomy barn, I could not see my cat.*

**gorge** /gôrj/ *n.* a deep, narrow valley with steep walls. *We kept our horses away from the edge of the deep gorge as we rode over the mountain trail.*

**gown** /goun/ *n.* a formal dress for a woman. *The gown she wore to the party sold at auction.*

**gra na ry** /grā′ nə rē/ *n., pl.* **granaries.** a place for storing grain. *Her farm's granary holds the livestock's feed.*

**gran ite** /gran′ it/ *n.* a hard rock containing quartz. *Granite is used in making monuments and other structures.*

**gull** /gul/ *n.* a bird found near the sea. *Gulls have long wings and gray and white feathers.*

**H**

**hem i sphere** /hem′ i sfir′/ *n.* one half of Earth. *The equator divides Earth into a Northern and a Southern hemisphere.*

**he red i ty** /hə red′ i tē/ *n.* family likeness. *Red hair and musical talent are part of my heredity.*

**her it age** /her′ i tij/ *n.* something handed down from the past; tradition. *Freedom of speech, the press, and religion are important parts of America's heritage.*

**high-pitched** /hī′ picht′/ *adj.* having a shrill sound. *The high-pitched cry of a bird flying overhead made the dog bark.*

**high-strung** /hī′ strung′/ *adj.* very tense or nervous by nature. *Some poodles can be rather high-strung animals.*

**home stead** /hōm′ sted′/ *n.* a farm or house with land. *The Homestead Act of 1862 gave 160 acres of free land to any head of a family who lived on the homestead for five years.*

**hon or** /on′ ər/ *v.* **honors, honoring, honored.** to pay respect to. *The school honored the teacher with a grand retirement party. n.* a sense of what is honest and right. *Washington was a man of honor and dignity.*

**hu mil i at ed** /hyoo mil′ ē ā′ təd/ *v.* a form of **humiliate.** to cause to seem foolish. *My mistake at the piano recital humiliated me.*

**I**

**ig ne ous** /ig′ nē əs/ *adj.* produced by great heat or volcanic action. *We found an igneous rock next to the inactive volcano.*

| | |
|---|---|
| /a/ | at |
| /ā/ | late |
| /â/ | care |
| /ä/ | father |
| /e/ | set |
| /ē/ | me |
| /i/ | it |
| /ī/ | kite |
| /o/ | ox |
| /ō/ | rose |
| /ô/ | brought |
| | raw |
| /oi/ | coin |
| /oo/ | book |
| /oo/ | too |
| /or/ | form |
| /ou/ | out |
| /u/ | up |
| /yoo/ | cube |
| /ûr/ | turn |
| | germ |
| | learn |
| | firm |
| | work |
| /ə/ | about |
| | chicken |
| | pencil |
| | cannon |
| | circus |
| /ch/ | chair |
| /hw/ | which |
| /ng/ | ring |
| /sh/ | shop |
| /th/ | thin |
| /th/ | there |
| /zh/ | treasure |

**im pres sive** /im pres′ iv/ *adj.* deserving of notice. *The student's impressive artwork helped her win an art scholarship.*

**im pulse** /im′ puls′/ *n.* quick action based on feeling. *After seeing* The Sound of Music, *I had an impulse to sing.*

**in come** /in′ kum′/ *n.* money taken in. *My income is spent on bills and food.*

**in cred i ble** /in kred′ ə bəl/ *adj.* **1.** hard or impossible to believe. *He told an incredible tale of being chased by five bandits.* **2.** amazing. *She had an incredible talent for making bird sounds.*

**in dif fer ent** /in dif′ ər ənt/ *adj.* uncaring; having or showing a lack of interest or concern. *The company president appeared indifferent to the long hours workers put in each day.*

**in di go** /in′ di gō′/ *n., pl.* **indigos,** or **indigoes.** a deep violet-blue color. *Indigo is one of the seven colors of the rainbow.*

**in dus tri ous** /in dus′ trē əs/ *adj.* hardworking. *The industrious student completed the weekend's homework on Friday evening.*

**in ex pen sive** /in′ ek spen′ siv/ *adj.* not costing much. *We always buy inexpensive sandals for the beach.*

**in fec tion** /in fek′ shən/ *n.* a disease caused by germs entering the body. *My uncle got an infection in his foot after he stepped on glass at the beach.*

**in fi nite** /in′ fə nit/ *adj.* **1.** having no limits. *There are an infinite number of stars in the universe.* **2.** very great. *The mathematician took infinite pains to check the equations in his work.*

**in flu ence** /in′ floo əns/ *n.* **1.** the power to affect others. *Teachers can have a great influence on their students.* **2.** a person or thing that has the power to affect others. *My older brother has been my greatest influence. v.* **influences, influencing, influenced.** to have an effect on; to serve as an example. *The astronaut's speech influenced me to study space science.*

**in form** /in form′/ *v.* **informs, informing, informed.** to give information to; to tell. *Please inform us of the time of your arrival at the airport.*

**in ject** /in jekt′/ *v.* **injects, injecting, injected.** **1.** to force a liquid through the skin or through a part of the body. *The polio vaccine was once injected into a person's arm.* **2.** to put or throw in. *The teacher tried to inject humor into the science lesson.*

**in quir y** /in kwīr′ ē/ *n., pl.* **inquiries.** **1.** a request for information. *I made an inquiry about the job notice at the grocery store.* **2.** an investigation. *The police department conducted an inquiry about the robbery.*

**in stinct** /in′ stingkt′/ *n.* inborn behavior; a way of acting that an animal or person is born with and does not learn. *Animals protecting their offspring is an instinct.*

**in ten tion** /in ten′ shən/ *n.* a purpose or plan. *My intention was to finish my homework by the time the baseball game started.*

**in ter cept** /in′ tər sept′/ *v.* **intercepts, intercepting, intercepted.** to stop or take something on its way from one person or place to another. *The teacher intercepts notes passed between friends.*

**in tern** /in´ tûrn/ *n.* a person who receives on-the-job training. *These journalism students were summer interns at the newspaper's main office.*

**in ter pret** /in tûr´ prit/ *v.* **interprets, interpreting, interpreted. 1.** to explain the meaning of. *My father said it would take an engineer to interpret the instructions that came with our new television.* **2.** to translate orally. *My sister interpreted the speaker's remarks from French into English for the class.*

**in ter rupt** /in´ tə rupt´/ *v.* **interrupts, interrupting, interrupted.** to cause a break in speech or action. *It is rude to interrupt someone when he or she is speaking.*

**in ter sect** /in´ tər sekt´/ *v.* **intersects, intersecting, intersected. 1.** to divide by cutting across or passing through. *A gorge intersects the mountain range.* **2.** to meet and cross each other. *Elm Street and Maple Avenue intersect near our house.*

**in vi ta tion** /in´ vi tā´ shən/ *n.* a spoken or written request to do something. *We mailed the invitations to my sister's graduation party.*

**irk** /ûrk/ *v.* **irks, irked.** to annoy or bother. *People who talk loudly in a library irk me.*

**ir ri gate** /ir´ i gāt´/ *v.* **irrigates, irrigating, irrigated.** to supply land with water. *Farmers irrigate their land through pipes or streams.*

**ir ri ta ble** /ir´ i tə bəl/ *adj.* close to getting angry. *Walking to the bus stop in the snow makes me irritable.*

**i vo ry** /ī´ və rē/ *n., pl.* **ivories.** a creamy white color. *Over time Grandma's white wedding dress has become ivory.*

**J**

**jeal ous** /jel´ əs/ *adj.* wanting what others have; envying what a person has or can do. *He was jealous of his friend's athletic ability.*

**L**

**la va** /lä´ və/ *n.* hot liquid rock from a volcano or an opening in Earth's surface. *Lava is more than 1,000° C and is hot enough to melt steel.*

**leg end ar y** /lej´ ən der´ ē/ *adj.* not real but thought true. *The Knights of the Round Table served the legendary English king, Arthur.*

**loan** /lōn/ *n.* something lent with promise to return. *We paid off our school loans five years after college.*

**lounge** /lounj/ *v.* **lounges, lounging, lounged.** to sit or lie around lazily. *After working all week, my family likes to lounge around the house on the weekend.*

| | |
|---|---|
| /a/ | at |
| /ā/ | late |
| /â/ | care |
| /ä/ | father |
| /e/ | set |
| /ē/ | me |
| /i/ | it |
| /ī/ | kite |
| /o/ | ox |
| /ō/ | rose |
| /ô/ | brought |
| | raw |
| /oi/ | coin |
| /o͝o/ | book |
| /o͞o/ | too |
| /or/ | form |
| /ou/ | out |
| /u/ | up |
| /yo͞o/ | cube |
| /ûr/ | turn |
| | germ |
| | learn |
| | firm |
| | work |
| /ə/ | about |
| | chicken |
| | pencil |
| | cannon |
| | circus |
| /ch/ | chair |
| /hw/ | which |
| /ng/ | ring |
| /sh/ | shop |
| /th/ | thin |
| /ᴛʜ/ | there |
| /zh/ | treasure |

**M** ▉▉▉▉▉▉▉▉▉▉▉▉▉▉▉▉

**ma roon** /mə rōōn′/ *v.* **maroons, marooning, marooned. 1.** to leave helpless and alone. *We found ourselves marooned on the road after a flood came through the city.* **2.** to leave alone on a deserted island. *A storm at sea marooned the sailor on the island for five days.*

**marsh** /märsh/ *n., pl.* **marshes.** low, wet land. *Grasses and plants called reeds grow in marshes.*

**mas ter piece** /mas′ tər pēs′/ *n.* something done with great skill. *The Dutch artist Van Gogh painted many beautiful masterpieces.*

**ma tu ri ty** /mə chŏŏr′ i tē/ *n., pl.* **maturities.** reaching full growth. *Taking responsibility for your actions is a sign of maturity.*

**mel low** /mel′ ō/ *adj.* **1.** calm. *Watching the sunset always leaves me feeling mellow.* **2.** ripe and sweet. *These mellow pears and berries will make a good dessert.*

**mi cro scop ic** /mī′ krə skop′ ik/ *adj.* very small. *The microscopic organism is so small that it can be seen only with special optical instruments.*

**min er al** /min′ ər əl/ *n.* a natural substance from the earth. *Minerals are not plants or animals.*

**min i mum** /min′ ə məm/ *n.* the least possible amount; the smallest amount. *We need a minimum of two days to build the tree house.*

**mi nor** /mī′ nər/ *adj.* lesser in size or degree. *The editor found a few minor mistakes.*

**mi nus** /mī′ nəs/ *prep.* **1.** reduced by; less. *Twelve minus two is ten.* **2.** lacking. *The kitchen table was minus a leg.*

**mod el** /mod′ əl/ *v.* **models, modeling, modeled. 1.** to use as an example. *The city council modeled the state senate when it set up procedures.* **2.** to make after a pattern. *This desk is modeled on the one used by Thomas Jefferson. n.* **1.** a sample of something. *Clay models are often made before large statues are built.* **2.** a style or type of thing. *My uncle's computer is an older model that works very well.*

**mon o gram** /mon′ ə gram′/ *n.* a design using two or more of a person's initials. *Monograms are used on clothing, towels, and stationery.*

**N** ▉▉▉▉▉▉▉▉▉▉▉▉▉▉▉▉

**nau se at ed** /nô′ zē ā′ tid/ *v.* to feel sickened. *The spinning of the carnival ride nauseated us.*

**ne ces si ty** /ni ses′ i tē/ *n., pl.* **necessities.** something needed; a requirement. *Shelter, food, and clothing are necessities of life.*

**O** ▉▉▉▉▉▉▉▉▉▉▉▉▉▉▉▉

**o a sis** /ō ā′ sis/ *n., pl.* **oases.** a fertile area in the desert. *Trees and plants can grow in an oasis because there is water available.*

**o be di ent** /ō bē′ dē ənt/ *adj.* willing to follow orders or rules. *After months of training and patience, we had obedient dogs.*

**ob sta cle** /ob′ stə kəl/ *n.* something or someone that stands in the way or blocks progress. *The fallen tree was an obstacle in the road.*

**of fen sive** /ə fen′ siv/ *adj.* rude or unpleasant. *I ignored my brother because of an offensive remark he made.*

**o pin ion** /ə pin′ yən/ *n.* a belief based on what someone thinks rather than on what is known to be true. *We need to get an expert's opinion before we buy a new computer.*

**op por tu ni ty** /ôp′ ər tōō′ ni tē/ *n., pl.* **opportunities.** a time or circumstance that is favorable or suitable for a particular purpose. *The audition is a great opportunity for your modeling career.*

**or ches tra** /or′ kə strə/ *n.* a group of musicians playing together on various instruments. *My brother plays the flute in the orchestra.*

**or i gin** /or′ i jin/ *n.* **1.** the starting point or cause of something. *The origin of the forest fire was the small fire of a careless camper.* **2.** parentage or ancestry. *My parents are of German origin.*

**out er most** /ou′ tər mōst′/ *adj.* farthest out. *There are times when Neptune is the outermost planet.*

**o ver haul** /ō′ vər hôl′/ *v.* **overhauls, overhauling, overhauled.** to look at closely and completely and repair. *Auto mechanics sometimes must overhaul a car's engine.*

**o ver pass** /ō′ vər pas′/ *n., pl.* **overpasses.** a bridge or road that cross over another road. *Some overpasses go over railroad tracks.*

**P** ▬▬▬▬▬▬▬▬

**par a mount** /par′ ə mount′/ *adj.* above all others; greatest. *My collection of model cars is of paramount importance to me.*

**pas sive** /pas′ iv/ *adj.* not active; acted upon without responding. *Our old collie became rather passive in his old age.*

**peas ant** /pez′ ənt/ *n.* a person who owns a small farm or works on a farm. *The peasants feasted with their families after a long hard day of working on their farms.*

**pen al ty** /pen′ əl tē/ *n., pl.* **penalties. 1.** a punishment. *The penalties for breaking the law can be severe.* **2.** punishment for a player or team for breaking the rules. *We groaned when the referee called a penalty against our team.*

**pe ri od i cal ly** /pir′ ē od′ ik lē/ *adv.* at regular times. *My father goes to London periodically on business.*

**per sist** /pər sist′/ *v.* **persists, persisting, persisted.** to continue steadily; to endure. *The rainy weather persisted for the rest of the week.*

**per suade** /pər swād′/ *v.* **persuades, persuading, persuaded.** to cause to do or believe something by pleading or giving reasons; to convince; to win over. *My friends persuaded me to go with them to help a neighbor move.*

| | |
|---|---|
| /a/ | at |
| /ā/ | late |
| /â/ | care |
| /ä/ | father |
| /e/ | set |
| /ē/ | me |
| /i/ | it |
| /ī/ | kite |
| /o/ | ox |
| /ō/ | rose |
| /ô/ | brought raw |
| /oi/ | coin |
| /o͝o/ | book |
| /o͞o/ | too |
| /or/ | form |
| /ou/ | out |
| /u/ | up |
| /yo͞o/ | cube |
| /ûr/ | turn germ learn firm work |
| /ə/ | about chicken pencil cannon circus |
| /ch/ | chair |
| /hw/ | which |
| /ng/ | ring |
| /sh/ | shop |
| /th/ | thin |
| /t͟h/ | there |
| /zh/ | treasure |

**pes si mis tic** /pes′ ə mis′ tik/ *adj.* expecting the worst. *Without my mother's help, I was pessimistic about being able to finish the quilt on time.*

**phy si cian** /fə zish′ ən/ *n.* a medical doctor. *A physician studies for many years to earn a license to treat sick and injured people.*

**pier** /pir/ *n.* a structure built out over the water, used especially as a landing place for boats and ships. *He waved to us from the end of the pier before getting into his boat.*

**pin point** /pin′ point′/ *v.* **pinpoints, pinpointing, pinpointed.** to locate or fix exactly. *A GPS device can pinpoint a location and display it on a small screen.*

**plan ta tion** /plan tā′ shən/ *n.* a large single-crop farm. *Cotton was once grown on plantations in the South.*

**pla teau** /pla tō′/ *n.,* **plateaus** or **plateaux.** an area of flat raised land. *A mesa is higher than a plateau.*

**plod** /plod/ *v.* **plods, plodding, plodded. 1.** to move slowly and heavily. *We had to plod through the deep snow on our way home from school.* **2.** to work slowly and steadily. *Over the weekend, I plodded through my history homework.*

**pluck** /pluk/ *v.* **plucks, plucking, plucked. 1.** to pull out or off. *The designer rapidly plucked the wilted flowers from the vases.* **2.** to pull and let go. *The musician plucked the strings of his guitar.*

**pop u lar i ty** /pop′ yə lar′ i tē/ *n., pl.* **popularities.** the condition of being widely liked. *The popularity of the doll resulted in shortages in all the toy stores.*

**praise** /prāz/ *v.* **praises, praising, praised.** to express admiration for. *He spent the entire dinner praising his favorite new music group. n.* words showing high approval and admiration. *Do not expect praise from me for that sloppy paint job!*

**pre vail** /pri vāl′/ *v.* **prevails, prevailing, prevailed. 1.** to be greater in power or influence; to win. *I say truth always prevails.* **2.** to be widespread. *Automobile accidents still prevail on the highways.*

**prism** /priz′ əm/ *n.* a transparent object that bends light rays. *A prism of glass or crystal bends light into the colors of the rainbow.*

**pri va cy** /prī′ və sē/ *n., pl.* **privacies. 1.** state of being alone or private. *I need privacy when I do my homework.* **2.** the right to be free from someone interfering in one's personal business. *There are laws to protect a person's privacy.*

**priv i lege** /priv′ ə lij/ *n.* a special right given to a person or to a group. *The older children were given the privilege of staying up late on Friday night.*

**pro fes sion al** /prə fesh′ ə nəl/ *adj.* of or relating to a person in a profession. *The doctor was offering free professional services. n.* a person engaged in a profession. *She is a long-term professional for our company.*

**pro gres sion** /prə gresh′ ən/ *n.* the act of advancing or moving ahead. *The fragile plant's progression was surprising everyone.*

**proj ect** /prə jekt′/ *v.* **projects, projecting, projected. 1.** to throw or propel forward. *An actor on stage projects his voice so that everyone in*

the audience can hear him.
**2.** to cause light or an image to fall on a surface. *A spotlight projects light onto a stage actor.* *n.* **proj ect** /proj′ ekt/ a plan or activity. *My school science project is about black holes in space.*

**pro mot ed** /prə mōt′əd/ *v.* a form of **promote. 1.** to raise in position or rank. *They promoted the captain to the rank of major.* **2.** to help in doing something. *Exercise and eating fewer fatty foods promote good health.*

**pros per ous** /pros′ pər əs/ *adj.* having success. *The prosperous town sent financial and material aid to flood victims in the southern part of the state.*

**pro test** /prə test′/ *v.* **protests, protesting, protested.** to express disapproval; to object to. *The students protested the early closing of the library. n.* /prō′ test/ a complaint or objection. *My mother ignored my protests for a bigger allowance.*

**pro vi sions** /prə vizh′ ənz/ *n. pl.* a supply of food. *We took provisions for five days on our camping trip.*

**pueb lo** /pweb′ lō/ *n., pl.* **pueblos. 1.** a Native American village. *The adobe and stone houses of a pueblo are joined in groups.* **2. Pueblo.** a member of a Native American tribe of New Mexico and Arizona. *The western group of*

Pueblo includes the Hopi and the Zuni.

**pyr a mid** /pir′ ə mid′/ *n.* a large stone structure used as a tomb. *A pyramid has a square base and triangular sides that meet at a point at the top.*

## Q

**quiv er** /kwiv′ ər/ *v.* **quivers, quivering, quivered.** to shake slightly. *The puppy quivered with excitement when we brought it home.*

## R

**rad i cal** /rad′ i kəl/ *n.* a person fighting for change. *My aunt was a radical during the antiwar movement of the 1960s. adj.* **1.** supporting basic changes in society. *Her radical beliefs sometimes caused arguments in her family.* **2.** basic. *Moving from a small school to a large one was a radical change in my life.*

**rec om mend** /rek′ ə mend′/ *v.* **1.** to speak of or present favorably. *He recommended the restaurant just around the corner.* **2.** to advise; suggest. *I recommend that you take a nap this afternoon.*

**re cov er** /ri kuv′ ər/ *v.* **recovers, recovering, recovered. 1.** to get back to a normal condition or position. *My brother is recovering from the mumps.* **2.** to get back, as in something lost; to regain. *We went back to recover our packs after they fell off our bicycles.*

| | |
|---|---|
| /a/ | at |
| /ā/ | late |
| /â/ | care |
| /ä/ | father |
| /e/ | set |
| /ē/ | me |
| /i/ | it |
| /ī/ | kite |
| /o/ | ox |
| /ō/ | rose |
| /ô/ | brought |
| | raw |
| /oi/ | coin |
| /o͝o/ | book |
| /o͞o/ | too |
| /or/ | form |
| /ou/ | out |
| /u/ | up |
| /yo͞o/ | cube |
| /ûr/ | turn |
| | germ |
| | learn |
| | firm |
| | work |
| /ə/ | about |
| | chicken |
| | pencil |
| | cannon |
| | circus |
| /ch/ | chair |
| /hw/ | which |
| /ng/ | ring |
| /sh/ | shop |
| /th/ | thin |
| /th̸/ | there |
| /zh/ | treasure |

**re cu per ate** /ri ko͞oʹ pə rātʹ/ *v.* **recuperates, recuperating, recuperated.** to gain back health after being sick. *My grandmother recuperated at our house after her illness.*

**re hears al** /ri hûrʹ səl/ *n.* the practice before a performance. *The orchestra had several rehearsals before the night of the concert.*

**re lax** /ri laksʹ/ *v.* **relaxes, relaxing, relaxed. 1.** to loosen. *To help your swing, relax your grip on the golf club.* **2.** to calm. *A swim in the pool usually relaxes me.*

**re mote** /ri mōtʹ/ *adj.* not near; far away in place or time. *After a long trek through the South American jungle, I finally reached the remote village.*

**re ply** /ri plīʹ/ *v.* **replies, replying, replied.** to answer or respond. *The governor has not yet replied to my letter. n.* an answer. *My reply to your question is in this letter.*

**re quest** /ri kwestʹ/ *v.* **requests, requesting, requested.** to ask or to ask for. *We requested permission to be excused. n.* the act of asking for something. *The mayor's request for a recount of the votes was granted.*

**re served** /ri zûrvdʹ/ *adj.* a form of **reserve. 1.** keeping feelings to oneself. *My grandfather is always polite and reserved.* **2.** set aside for a purpose. *Call the restaurant to get a reserved table.*

**res er voir** /rezʹ ər vwärʹ/ *n.* a place for water storage. *Many cities use water from reservoirs.*

**res o lu tion** /rezʹ ə lo͞oʹ shən/ *n.* solution; something decided upon. *Our family's resolution is to eat dinner together more often.*

**rug ged** /rugʹ id/ *adj.* **1.** having a rough and uneven surface. *The rugged mountains rose in the background over the valley below.* **2.** hard to put up with; harsh. *Early American pioneers led a rugged life.*

**ru ral** /ro͝orʹ əl/ *adj.* relating to or like the country. *Rural areas have farms and are not crowded with people.*

**S** ▆▆▆▆▆▆▆▆▆▆▆▆▆

**sac ri fice** /sakʹ rə fīsʹ/ *v.* **sacrifices, sacrificing, sacrificed.** to give up something that is valued or wanted for the sake of something else. *Parents sacrifice to give their children what they need.*

**sal a ry** /salʹ ə rē/ *n., pl.* **salaries.** a fixed amount of payment for work. *Workers in the computer industry often receive high salaries.*

**sales per son** /sālzʹ pûrʹ sən/ *n., pl.* **salespeople.** one who sells goods or services. *The salesperson gave us a detailed list of the bicycle's features.*

**sal vage** /salʹ vij/ *v.* **salvages, salvaging, salvaged.** to save from being destroyed or lost. *Very little was salvaged from the* Titanic *when the ship sank in 1912.*

**sanc tu ar y** /sangkʹ cho͞o erʹ ē/ *n., pl.* **sanctuaries.** a place of protection. *A bird sanctuary is a safe place for hundreds of birds to make their homes.*

**scene** /sēn/ *n.* **1.** the place and time in which the action of a story occurs. *The play's scene was the South during the Civil War.* **2.** the place where something happens. *The police raced to the scene of the crime.*

**scheme** /skēm/ *n.* **1.** a secret plan for doing something. *The police found out about the scheme to rob their mayor's house.* **2.** an orderly arrangement of things. *The color scheme in our house is green and white.*

**scorch** /skorch/ *v.* **scorches, scorching, scorched. 1.** to burn slightly. *Be careful not to scorch your shirt when you iron it.* **2.** to burn with heat. *The summer sun has scorched our lawn.*

**sec tion** /sek′ shən/ *n.* **1.** a part of something cut off from the rest; a portion. *This section of the roast is for tomorrow's dinner.* **2.** a part of something written. *She reads the newspaper's arts section first.*

**sed i men tar y** /sed′ə men′ tə rē/ *adj.* formed from particles of stone or animal remains deposited over millions of years. *Layers of sedimentary rock were formed by water, wind, and ice.*

**sel dom** /sel′ dəm/ *adv.* not often. *I seldom interrupt other people when they are talking.*

**sen sa tion** /sen sā′ shən/ *n.* **1.** something that causes excitement. *The magician caused a sensation when he jumped through the hoop of fire onstage.* **2.** a feeling or state of being aware. *A sensation of fear went through me when I heard the lion roar in the African jungle.*

**ses sion** /sesh′ ən/ *n.* **1.** a period of time. *Our sessions with the dog trainer have helped prepare my dog for the dog show.* **2.** a meeting of a group. *The first session of the Supreme Court begins on the first Monday in October.*

**shade** /shād/ *v.* **shades, shading, shaded. 1.** to darken. *The artist shaded the faces of the people in her drawing with a pencil.* **2.** to shelter or protect. *A beach umbrella shades you from the sun. n.* **1.** something that shuts out light. *I lowered the shades in my room to keep out the sun.* **2.** a place sheltered from the sun. *We sat in the shade of a large oak tree.*

**shame** /shām/ *n.* embarrassment from wrongdoings or foolishness. *The student felt shame for having cheated on the test.*

**shriv el** /shriv′ əl/ *v.* **shrivels, shriveling, shriveled.** to shrink and become wrinkled. *Fruit shrivels when it is dried.*

**shrug** /shrug/ *v.* **shrugs, shrugging, shrugged.** to raise up the shoulders. *He shrugs his shoulders when he does not know the answer.*

**slang** /slang/ *n.* an informal kind of language used in everyday conversation. *Slang is often used for a short time and sometimes disappears from a language.*

**slate** /slāt/ *n.* a bluish-gray rock. *Slate is used to make blackboards.*

| | |
|---|---|
| /a/ | at |
| /ā/ | late |
| /â/ | care |
| /ä/ | father |
| /e/ | set |
| /ē/ | me |
| /i/ | it |
| /ī/ | kite |
| /o/ | ox |
| /ō/ | rose |
| /ô/ | brought |
| | raw |
| /oi/ | coin |
| /o͝o/ | book |
| /o͞o/ | too |
| /or/ | form |
| /ou/ | out |
| /u/ | up |
| /yo͞o/ | cube |
| /ûr/ | turn |
| | germ |
| | learn |
| | firm |
| | work |
| /ə/ | about |
| | chicken |
| | pencil |
| | cannon |
| | circus |
| /ch/ | chair |
| /hw/ | which |
| /ng/ | ring |
| /sh/ | shop |
| /th/ | thin |
| /ŧh/ | there |
| /zh/ | treasure |

**so cial ize** /sō′ shə līz′/ *v.* to enjoy the company of others and take part in social activities. *The meeting started late because everyone was socializing.*

**so phis ti cat ed** /sə fis′ ti kā′ tid/ *adj.* a form of **sophisticate.** having worldly experience. *My sister is a sophisticated traveler because she has been to Europe five times.*

**spe cial ist** /spesh′ ə list/ *n.* an expert. *My uncle is a specialist in the field of sports medicine.*

**spon ta ne ous** /spon tā′ nē əs/ *adj.* not planned. *When the bus arrived, there was spontaneous applause from the passengers.*

**stalk** /stôk/ *v.* **stalks, stalking, stalked. 1.** to hunt or track down. *The tiger slowly and quietly stalks its prey.* **2.** to walk in a stiff manner. *She turned and stalked out of the room.*

**stern** /stûrn/ *adj.* **1.** firm, unmoving. *The stern will of the climbers kept them moving up the mountain.* **2.** strict or severe. *The coach's stern expression told the players what he thought about their performance.*

**strat e gy** /strat′ i jē/ *n., pl.* **strategies.** a plan for achieving a goal. *Our team needs a strategy to win the next game.*

**stream lined** /strēm′ līnd′/ *adj.* smooth and efficient in design. *The streamlined look of some sports cars gives them a futuristic appearance.*

**strug gle** /strug′ əl/ *v.* **struggles, struggling, struggled.** to put forth a great effort. *I struggled to learn some of the Spanish language over the summer.*

**stub born** /stub′ ərn/ *adj.* **1.** not giving in. *The stubborn horse refused to cross the river.* **2.** hard to deal with. *My stubborn cold lasted two weeks.*

**styl ish** /stī′ lish/ *adj.* according to the current fashion. *Fashion models usually wear stylish clothes.*

**sub se quent** /sub′ si kwənt/ *adj.* happening after. *Her subsequent promotion proved that she had been doing good work.*

**sub ur ban** /sə bûr′ bən/ *adj.* relating to the area just outside a city; relating to the suburbs. *The suburban area lies between the countryside and the city.*

**sulk y** /sul′ kē/ *adj.* stubbornly silent or withdrawn as a display of bad humor or anger. *We tried to cheer up the sulky child.*

**surge** /sûrj/ *v.* **surges, surging, surged.** to swell and move forward. *The crowd at the gate surged forward.*

**sur geon** /sûr′ jən/ *n.* a medical doctor who performs operations. *Surgeons often have strong, steady hands.*

**sur vey** /sər vā′/ *v.* **surveys, surveying, surveyed. 1.** to look at as a whole. *From a helicopter the governor surveyed the land damaged by the hurricane.* **2.** to study in detail. *The builder surveyed the property before he began excavating.* /sûr′ vā/ *n.* a questionnaire or detailed study. *The library conducted a survey to find out what people were reading.*

**sus pend** /sə spend′/ *v.* **suspends, suspending, suspended. 1.** to hold in place. *The trapeze artist was suspended in midair as he swung between two bars.* **2.** to attach so as to hang down. *We suspended an old tire from a tree to make a swing.*

**syn chro nize** /sing′ krə nīz′/ *v.* **synchronizes, synchronizing, synchronized. 1.** to happen at the same time. *The swimmers synchronized their movements in the water.* **2.** to make timepieces agree. *Let's synchronize our watches so we arrive at the same time.*

**syn thet ic** /sin thet′ ik/ *adj.* made by humans. *Plastic is a synthetic material that is molded when it is soft.*

## T

**tem ple** /tem′ pəl/ *n.* a building used for worshipping a god or gods. *You can see the ruins of ancient temples in Greece.*

**ten sion** /ten′ shən/ *n.* mental or nervous strain. *Worrying or working too much causes tension.*

**ter rain** /tə rān′/ *n.* a region of land or ground. *The rocky terrain made it difficult for the hikers to walk fast.*

**ter ri to ry** /ter′ i tor′ ē/ *n., pl.* **territories.** any large area of land. *There is not much unexplored territory left in the world.*

**tex tile** /teks′ tīl/ *n.* a woven or knitted cloth. *Textiles are used for rugs, bedspreads, and clothing.*

**tex ture** /teks′ chər/ *n.* the look and feel of a woven fabric or other material. *Silk has a smooth, soft texture.*

**ti ar a** /tē ar′ ə/ *n.* a crownlike piece worn on the head. *Queens and princesses often wear tiaras at formal events.*

**tide wa ter** /tīd′ wô′ tər/ *n.* **1.** water brought up by the tide. *The tidewater covered the edge of the lawn of the beach cottage.* **2.** low-lying coastal land where the water is affected by tides. *There is tidewater along the coast of Virginia.*

**tinge** /tinj/ *v.* **tinges, tingeing, tinged.** to add a little color to. *The artist tinged her painting of the sunset with a shade of pink.*

**tran quil** /trang′ kwəl/ *adj.* peaceful and calm. *A tranquil place is one that is quiet and restful.*

**trans mit** /trans mit′/ *v.* **transmits, transmitting, transmitted. 1.** to send or pass from one person or place to another. *Some diseases can be transmitted by contact with an infected person.* **2.** to send out signals by radio or television. *This radio station transmits the news and weather all day.*

**trans par ent** /trans pâr′ ənt/ *adj.* easily seen through. *Most windows in homes are made with transparent glass.*

**treat ment** /trēt′ mənt/ *n.* **1.** a plan for treating sickness. *Treatment for a cold includes getting rest and drinking plenty of liquids.* **2.** the way something or someone is treated. *The treatment I get from my grandparents is always that of kindness.*

| | |
|---|---|
| /a/ | at |
| /ā/ | late |
| /â/ | care |
| /ä/ | father |
| /e/ | set |
| /ē/ | me |
| /i/ | it |
| /ī/ | kite |
| /o/ | ox |
| /ō/ | rose |
| /ô/ | brought raw |
| /oi/ | coin |
| /o͝o/ | book |
| /o͞o/ | too |
| /or/ | form |
| /ou/ | out |
| /u/ | up |
| /yo͞o/ | cube |
| /ûr/ | turn germ learn firm work |
| /ə/ | about chicken pencil cannon circus |
| /ch/ | chair |
| /hw/ | which |
| /ng/ | ring |
| /sh/ | shop |
| /th/ | thin |
| /ᵺ/ | there |
| /zh/ | treasure |

**trust wor thy** /trust′ wûr ᵗħē/ *adj.* reliable; able to be depended on. *The trustworthy tugboat pushed the ship into the harbor.*

**tux e do** /tuk sē′ dō/ *n.*, *pl.* **tuxedos.** a formal suit for a man. *The trousers of a tuxedo have a satin stripe along the side of each leg.*

**U**

**ul ti mate ly** /ul′ tə mit lē/ *adv.* in the end. *After a summer in Denmark, my efforts to learn Danish ultimately paid off.*

**un bear a ble** /un bâr′ ə bəl/ *adj.* very hard to put up with. *Life in the Arctic may be unbearable at times.*

**un cer tain** /un sûr′ tən/ *adj.* **1.** not sure. *The outcome of the presidential race was uncertain for weeks.* **2.** changing. *The weather in April is often uncertain.*

**un der hand ed** /un′ dər han′ did/ *adj.* done in a secretive or sneaky manner. *What is the criminal's latest underhanded trick?*

**un speak a ble** /un spē′ kə bəl/ *adj.* too bad to talk about. *The car accident was an unspeakable tragedy.*

**ur ban** /ûr′ bən/ *adj.* relating to or like a city. *Urban areas usually have many buildings, buses, and people.*

**V**

**va cant** /vā′ kənt/ *adj.* unoccupied or empty. *Almost half the seats in the arena were vacant for the performance.*

**var i a tion** /vâr′ ē ā′ shən/ *n.* the amount of difference. *The variation in temperature between yesterday and today is twenty degrees.*

**vel vet** /vel′ vit/ *n.* a cloth with smooth, thick fibers. *The chair made of velvet was cozy.*

**ven ture** /ven′ chər/ *v.* **ventures, venturing, ventured.** to do regardless of the risk. *We ventured into the woods and did not worry about getting lost.* *n.* something that involves risk. *No one knows whether the new business venture will make money.*

**vi sor** /vī′ zər/ *n.* the front brim of a cap that shades the eyes. *To keep the sun out of his eyes, the golfer wore a hat with a visor.*

**W**

**ward robe** /word′ rōb′/ *n.* a collection of clothing. *The theater company had a large costume wardrobe.*

**waste land** /wāst′ land′/ *n.* an area with few or no living things. *Desert areas and polar regions are wastelands.*

**wide spread** /wīd′ spred′/ *adj.* extending over a large area. *The widespread forest fire caused much damage to the state.*

**wist ful** /wist′ fəl/ *adj.* sadly wishing or longing. *Seeing people walking their dogs made me wistful for a puppy.*

**wrong do ing** /rông′ doo′ ing/ *n.* bad behavior; the act of doing something wrong. *My parents talked to me about my wrongdoing.*

# A—F Word Bank

# G—M Word Bank

# N—S Word Bank

_____  _____

_____  _____

_____  _____

_____  _____

_____  _____

_____  _____

_____  _____

_____  _____

_____  _____

_____  _____

_____  _____

_____  _____

_____  _____

_____  _____

_____  _____

_____  _____

_____  _____

_____  _____

# T—Z Word Bank